SCIENCE, GOVERNMENT, AND THE UNIVERSITIES

SCIENCE,
GOVERNMENT,
AND THE UNIVERSITIES

Introduction by
FREDERICK SEITZ
President, National Academy of Sciences

Seattle and London, 1966
UNIVERSITY OF WASHINGTON PRESS

Publisher's Foreword

Each year the National Academy of Sciences, to which scientists and engineers are elected on the basis of distinguished contribution to fundamental research in science or technology, holds an autumn meeting at the invitation of some educational or research institution at which work is being done under the leadership of Academy members. In autumn 1965, the Academy met at the University of Washington and one of the features of the scientific program was the symposium on "Science, Government, and the Universities" organized by Dr. Hans Neurath, Chairman of the University of Washington Department of Biochemistry and Chairman of the Program Committee. This volume consists of contributions to that symposium and two addresses delivered at the meeting that also illuminated the subject of the symposium.

Contents

*PART ONE: Symposium on Science,
Government, and the Universities*

Introduction   3
FREDERICK SEITZ

A Look Ahead   8
DONALD F. HORNIG

The Role of the University
in the Exploration of Space   26
+HUGH L. DRYDEN

Some Problems and Trends
in the Support of Academic Science   42
LELAND J. HAWORTH

Biomedical Sciences—
Present Status and Problems   61
JAMES A. SHANNON

PART TWO: Two Views from the University

Humanistic Aspects of Science   73
CHARLES E. ODEGAARD

Science and Government—
Opportunities and Conflicts   84
PHILIP HANDLER

Appendix: Strengthening Academic Capability
for Science Throughout the Nation   109
LYNDON B. JOHNSON

Part One

SYMPOSIUM ON SCIENCE,
GOVERNMENT, AND THE UNIVERSITIES

FREDERICK SEITZ

President, National Academy of Sciences

Introduction

Modern science evolved in western Europe over many centuries, starting at a time soon after the Crusades. To identify the initial incentives for the development of modern science in western European society would be a complex and difficult task; on the whole, the process is relatively obscure. The facts remain, however, that in the particular climate which occurred in western Europe during the medieval and then the Renaissance period, science did grow and eventually produce one of the most remarkable revolutions in human history, comparable to the agricultural revolution associated with the development of the great river valleys. As the development progressed, particularly following the ferment of the Renaissance, it became so deeply linked to the European pattern of life—a life centering around scholarly, cultural, and technical affairs—that it is impossible for us now to imagine European life without modern science.

During the first half of the nineteenth century, as

the industrial revolution took hold in central Europe, it was discovered that scientific research had a natural place in the evolution of the pattern of higher education in the universities. This led to the development of a close link in western Europe among universities, government, and science. Since the universities there accepted governmental support in the last century, the issue scarcely arose as a distinct policy question. This idea of government support for science and the universities was often discussed, but rarely in an atmosphere of crisis, since it was apparently taken as more or less a matter of natural evolution.

Affairs have been quite different on this side of the Atlantic, in spite of the fact that our links with Europe are well defined. Most individuals in our country are descended from *émigrés* of essentially the same geographic areas in which science had developed. But there have been significant deviations from the European pattern—for example, the concept of valuing knowledge for its own sake, which has been of enormous import in the European pattern, did not develop on a comparable scale on this side of the Atlantic. Certainly through most of the last century, and until recently, creative science was regarded as something of a stepchild in our country. Our own industrial revolution—which was far from a trivial one—depended in the main on importation of basic ideas from western Europe. These ideas were coupled with access to a vast quantity of inexpensive raw materials, and that great quality, referred to as Yankee ingenuity, which permits us to produce new things quickly. Because the

population density in our large country was sufficiently low relative to that of Europe, as the industrial
revolution progressed it was possible to dedicate our
resources to the concept of bringing the products of
mass production to almost everyone, a feat which
western Europe achieved much more slowly and, in
fact, has accomplished in the main only since World
War II.

The fundamental appreciation of basic science in
our social structure became noticeable around the turn
of the present century. There was, for example, the
creation of the great industrial laboratories—the Bell
Telephone Laboratory, the General Electric Research
Laboratory, the DuPont Laboratories, and others—all
about 1900. At approximately the same time, a few of
our academic institutions, in a more or less sporadic
way, began to recognize scientific research as an essential part of higher education. The sporadic nature
of this trend is demonstrated by the fact that the first
three American citizens to win the Nobel Prize in
physics were for the most part associated in their productive careers with one institution—the University of
Chicago—which was, remarkably enough, created in
1890 following a somewhat revolutionary pattern.

Outside of agricultural research, in which the practical side has been prominent for over a century, science in the transitional period around the beginning
of the century was of interest largely to private or
state groups. The federal government played a very
small role, although it did take the significant step of
creating the National Bureau of Standards. Viewed in

perspective, our academic institutions were on the whole not very distinguished before 1900 when compared to their European counterparts. Many of them had started as sectarian schools with the goal of training people for the clergy. As they evolved, they added law, the teaching profession, and medicine; however, before 1900, their growth tended to focus in a rather narrow way on certain fields of professional specialization, rather than on scholarship in a broad sense. All this changed following 1900, slowly though significantly in the period between 1900 and 1939, and then most rapidly since 1945 with the help of federal funds, particularly in areas related to science.

Today, some twenty years after the end of World War II, we are not only in the midst of a great revolution in the relationship among the universities, science, and the federal government, but many of our scientists are compelled in the interest of public welfare to grapple with the basic issues involved in this revolution. These individuals must try to assess the significance of trends and to provide some degree of guidance to them, admitting that it is difficult to understand all facets of the revolution, let alone to gain control of the trends.

The conflict between new and old traditions was vividly illustrated to me most recently by a discussion I had with an important public figure in Washington, a man who is deeply involved with the process of providing money for science. Speaking to me of the problems in his work, he said, "The difficulty I have to face with my colleagues is this—for about five years the physical sciences haven't produced a new break-through, and they say, 'Well this would be a good time to cut back.' "

Since 1939 or 1940, when our federal government began supporting the physical sciences in a serious way, the physical sciences have brought to the nation three significant revolutions in the field of military science and technology alone. I would have thought that there would be no doubt that the physical scientists, for one, had earned the right of support for the remainder of this century. Yet in the environment in which we live today, this can be seriously questioned by men in responsible positions.

The changes that are taking place at present—and I believe that we are in midstream—are so rapid that new concepts impinge significantly upon old ones deeply rooted in our national traditions. Clearly, we are in one way or another evolving an entirely new set of national traditions under conditions in which old viewpoints die hard and in which a climate of struggle is apparent. I would guess that this struggle will continue for at least another twenty years, by which time the new traditions—whatever they may be—will probably have achieved something in the nature of a steady state.

Let us turn now to a number of our colleagues who are very much concerned with these problems, men who have dedicated much of their careers to consideration of the interrelation of the universities, science, and the federal government.

DONALD HORNIG

Special Assistant to the President
for Science and Technology

A Look Ahead

T<small>HE</small> relationship between the federal government and the universities has been a developing partnership in the public service, a partnership which has proved extraordinarily fruitful for the universities, for the government, for science, and, above all, for the nation we serve. I would like to take stock of the benefits, as well as some liabilities which have arisen from this partnership, and to look ahead at its future development.

In historical perspective, it is clear that the over-all progress in science is marked here and there by peaks of achievement, true breakthroughs in sometimes unsuspected directions. These peaks rest on a broad and expanding base of solid growth. The central problem in fostering scientific progress, therefore, is how best to encourage the breakthroughs while maintaining the greatest possible rate of growth, in both quality and quantity, at the base. Even in the most abstract terms, such considerations revolve ultimately, so far as the federal government is concerned, around the problem of financial support. In the first instance, we as a nation must decide how much of our funds to allocate to science; in the second, how to allocate them; and in the third, by what specific mechanisms to distribute the funds in order best to accomplish the goals we have set. Such reasoning clearly implies that the future shape of science and the directions of its progress will be determined not only by the scientific community but by the nation as a whole. As in all human affairs, the people who foot the bills are entitled to determine how they want to spend their money.

Let us take a closer look at some of these problems. This relationship between science and the public, or more directly between the universities and the federal government, first became intimate during World War II and has since grown to very substantial proportions. About three fourths of all university research, one third of all graduate students in science, and a majority of the students in the final phases of their Ph.D. research, are now supported by the federal government, and federal funds pay for about one third of the cost of all new science facilities. Recently this support has been extended by various new programs of the National Science Foundation to bring training and participation in research to college teachers and undergraduates. The many federal programs of support for science involve about four hundred colleges and universities, including all Ph.D.-granting institutions in the country.

When these programs are compared to those of

any other country in the world, we note one very striking difference. Except for the Department of Agriculture, they have not provided for the allotment of funds by formula, either of population or geography. They have not provided for distribution of funds by institution, as in the British university grant system. By and large they have rested on the identification of talented, promising individuals and groups of individuals, on the identification of worthwhile, creative, original, and significant researches, in large measure proposed by individuals. In short, we have attempted to operate a system based on talent and on merit of individuals. Naturally, judgments of merit are hard to make. The evaluations of proposals have in some cases—such as in the NIH and NSF—been carried out by study sections and panels of scientists. Such judgment by peers has been widely commended in every study which has been undertaken. I note particularly that of the National Academy of Sciences Committee on Science and Public Policy, "Federal Support of Basic Research in Institutions of Higher Learning" and the Wooldridge study of the NIH, which was undertaken for the President. However, other agencies have sought to achieve a similar goal through the use of internal consultants or staff judgments. Whether or not the approach was consistently correct in its judgment, it was basically sound in that it focused attention on excellence and merit wherever they were found—in whatever state or whatever institution—and in that way avoided many of the difficult questions posed by institutional choices. I consider this approach a major invention in the government support of science and one that is in no small measure responsible for the great success we have had.

Another invention of great significance has been the network of advisory panels, groups, committees, and boards established to provide advice on the award of federal grants and contracts. The primary function of these groups is to provide scientifically competent and unbiased advice to the federal agencies. They have performed this function well. But they have done much more. The advisory groups have involved scientists in large numbers from many universities in the making of decisions. This wide participation has played a large part in preventing the kind of split between the universities and the federal government that many feared after World War II. In addition, these advisory groups have been in significant but unanticipated way a major means of strengthening the informal communication among scientists. The advisory system inevitably generates problems, such as the possibility of lack of objectivity. But on the whole, the entire structure has contributed in an important way to the health of the existing federal system for the support of research.

This way of doing things, this emphasis on merit and excellence, this concentration on the individual and on the proposed research rather than on the institution has raised some problems. But it has been the backbone of our system. It has provided a degree of freedom for the individual research worker and scientists, particularly for younger men, a freedom from administrative restraints, both within the university and within the government, that is in my mind unmatched anywhere. It has brought great vitality and energy to our scientific enterprise. It has held out the prospect of support to all capable individuals no matter where in the country they are located. There will be changes, but I am sure that this primary emphasis on quality and upon the individual must and will remain the backbone of our government relations with the universities.

I do not believe that I can demonstrate that either the quantity or the mode of federal support is wholly responsible for the extraordinary progress of American science in the last two decades. Nevertheless, the fact that science has flourished is unquestioned. This period has seen the interpretation of living systems in terms of chemical reactions and structure of molecules take hold in a way which promises to place biology on a theoretical and experimental foundation as secure as that of chemistry and physics in the past. It has seen elementary particle physics step out into an unknown realm which makes the revolution of physical understanding in the 1920's only a prelude to much more fundamental problems toward which we can only grope. That ancient science, astronomy, has burst forward with a new vigor as both radio and optical astronomers discover new and fantastic objects on the outermost borders of space. The advent of space astronomy has already given us a new knowledge of x-ray sources and promises to open up spectral regions heretofore closed to us. Earth scientists have begun to investigate the entire atmosphere of the earth as a system, and to study the structure and the dynamics of the entire earth, so that the pace of our understanding advances by leaps and bounds. This has surely been a period of extraordinary progress.

Why, then, if things are going well should we not simply continue doing what has been successful? Many scientists feel precisely this way—particularly those who have profited from the approach—and they are very concerned at the prospect of change. But there will be change, because our very success and growth have changed the situation. The progress of science has accelerated the development of the society which science serves. For example, one of the most striking characteristics of the university scene today is the growth of new, strong centers of scholarship and research. In the fields I know, quite aside from statistical data, there are many more good schools than there were two decades ago. What is even more striking is the growth of the ambition to be excellent, the ambition to be strong. All over the country, schools that in the past awarded no advanced degrees, or at best a few, and whose faculties were little concerned with scholarship, are now on the road to academic excellence. They have recruited or are recruiting stronger faculties, building new facilities, and they aspire to compete on their own terms with the established centers of strength. These schools want help and deserve help and, if given the support they need, will in many cases achieve the kind of excellence which has been realized by the best of the older institutions. They will eventually compete for their share of research support on the traditional terms, but they may need some investment before they reach that happy state.

Another factor which has caused some concern is that as federal dollars become a considerable part of the budget of an institution their effect may be to distort the internal structure of universities as educational institutions. I am worried that having freed the creative and talented investigator from the petty bureaucracy of the departmental tyrant, we have also helped remove him from the university as a whole and have turned science departments into a collection of feudal fiefs rather than organic wholes.

Then there is the concern over the effect of our great research programs on undergraduate education. Curiously, these arguments take two quite different forms. On the one hand, it is felt that good undergraduate education can only be given in institutions where creative minds are at work and scholarly activity goes forward, where the students can sense the pulse and thrust of important enterprise and motion. It is argued that institutions that do not carry on enough research cannot recruit the faculties to provide a first-class education. On the other hand, it is sometimes argued that within institutions in which research and advanced education are active, the faculties lose all interest in undergraduates and leave them to junior members of the faculty. Surely, both cannot be true, and if they are, we should be able to devise a better way of doing things.

In my view the general situation is something like this. We set out two decades ago—realizing that scientific and technological advance were the foundation for the nation's health, for its economy, for its secure defense, and for many other purposes—to strengthen the scientific foundations of the country. This is still our conviction, so one of our big jobs is to strengthen and develop workers and institutions that can advance our knowledge and understanding and carry on researches at the very forefront of man's knowledge. The accomplishment of this goal with finite resources requires that we find the most able and talented students, give them the very best teachers, and provide them with tools which can accomplish the job. To attain this goal, we must select and concentrate our most talented students at institutions where they can study with inspired teachers and researchers and where we can build up the necessary facilities and experimental equipment. The spires of supreme scientific achievement were erected by this historical method, which was the pattern that continued to be followed in the early days of federal support. What is more, for the purpose of producing the very best science, for the purpose of penetrating the frontiers of ignorance, such pinnacles of achievement are a proper and necessary part of the scene and will be in the future.

To put the matter more clearly, let me use an analogy. This nation wants deeply to have its share of Olympic gold medals. We want to win a majority of the events. To produce Olympic athletes, no amount of running little boys around the block will suffice. We have to find those with real talent and concentrate the care of our best coaches upon them. We must concentrate the best education to develop the mental gymnasts as well. But there is another side to this coin. To follow my analogy, we could not hope to recruit the skilled athletes without a national physical fitness program to build up the skills of all the children so that the potential champions can be selected for intensive training. Similarly, in the intellectual sphere it is important, if we are to identify the most able and best qualified, that there be academic strength throughout the country. For this purpose we must not only maintain and increase the pinnacles of outstanding achievement, but we must build up a strong base. This is a philosophy the President has repeatedly proclaimed, and it is surely the key to the future, at least for this administration.

These generalities are all very well, but I would like to look a little deeper into the guides we can find for the directions we are going and ought to go to achieve the best balance between these factors. When science was a small enterprise, it was easy to think in terms of selecting a few gifted individuals and backing them. But it has now become a very large enterprise. The nation invests several billion dollars a year in research, 1.3 billion of that in universities proper, not counting the accelerator laboratories and other attached institutions. As a consequence, the shape of science and the directions of scientific progress are no longer a matter for the scientific community alone;

they have become part of the public enterprise. We must face the fact that now and in the future the Congress and the public, who respectively appropriate the money which supports us and pay the bill, expect to be heard as we set our course for the future. And this is quite properly so.

This has led me to ask why the American public is in fact willing to spend so much on scientific research and on scientific education. Part of the reason is the expectation of future benefits. Certainly the appropriations for research in the biomedical sciences, no matter how abstract, are supported in the public mind in the expectation of future improvements to health, cures for diseases, longer and more fruitful life, and so forth. The rapid expansion of support and the big proportion of our efforts which go in this direction reflect only in part the judgment of the scientific community that this is a fruitful area of understanding, ripe for great progress. We should realize that the rapid growth came about in the fifties through the action of the Congress, particularly Senator Lister Hill and Congressman John E. Fogarty, who insisted on appropriating more funds than the executive branch and many scientists thought wise. A later study of a representative sample of projects by a distinguished panel, which indicated that the funds had been extremely well spent, shows the conservatism of many scientists. This is clearly one case where the public was right.

The public has come to accept the argument that progress flows from basic science and that material and social benefits in the future derive from the most abstract investigations today. It has come to accept the belief that the health and intellectual tone of a community or a region are improved by the presence of strong and vigorous universities. Beyond the expectation of practical results, there is the very sincere and general conviction, which has been expressed so often by the President, that the twentieth century is a century of science and technology, and that the progress of applied science depends on the constant replenishment of its sources of new ideas. I think the public well understands that we have no idea from what obscure basis the critical new discoveries may come. And this may be the reason that, much as in my analogy to the Olympic games, we find a general national determination that we should be first, or at least in the forefront, of every field of science—from mathematics to space, to high-energy physics, biology, and so forth. It would be wrong to underestimate the public interest in the pure intellectual achievements of science. I am constantly struck by the fact that pronouncements on science policy or promises of new practical benefits often attract only the slightest attention in the press, but that the measurement of the occultation of the crab nebula by the moon for the purpose of discovering whether the x-ray source there is a point source or diffused throughout the nebula can occupy two columns of the Washington papers.

To summarize, the situation is this. We have several, perhaps about twenty, really outstanding institutions which set the tone and standard for the whole enterprise. This number will grow, but we will always look to a limited number of institutions to perform this function. Our scientific support has been concentrated in the direction of those institutions, but as science becomes increasingly a public matter, there is a spreading desire by all parts of the country to share in the material and intellectual benefits which spring from strong science and strong universities. Now, where does this leave us, and where are we going? There are a variety of winds blowing, but I believe that the dominating philosophy I have mentioned will persist and that all our policies will be directed to two things: first, that we want to be at the forefront of every major field of scientific advance, and second, that the whole nation wants to participate in the process.

For the present, the first goal has been achieved. But this is a competitive world, and to maintain the excellence of our science we will continue to back the best brains wherever we find them. We will surely continue, as the President said at Brown University, to support those institutions which provide the superior training for the teachers and researchers who go from them to the aspiring institutions and who will provide the core around which the new institutions will grow. We are less satisfied with our progress toward the second objective, which is to provide the best possible advanced education in enough institutions so that able American children from all backgrounds and from all parts of the country have an opportunity to participate in the best that science and the modern world have to offer. It is clear, therefore, that there will be a major emphasis on improving education as well as science.

It was with this in mind that the President recently sent a memorandum to the heads of all departments and agencies in the government, most of which spend their funds for the primary purpose of producing scientific advance in those areas of science of basic concern in achieving their agency goals. The memorandum, "Strengthening Academic Capability for Science Throughout the Nation,"* is an instruction that in the course of spending money for these purposes, all of the agencies should recognize and consider the impact that their expenditures have on the higher educational system of the country, and adjust their practices so as to do the most possible for higher education. Specifically, I quote from some of the President's instructions:

> Our policies and attitudes in regard to science cannot satisfactorily be related solely to achievement of goals and ends we set for our research. Our vision in this regard is limited at best. We must, I believe, devote ourselves purposefully to developing and diffusing—throughout the nation—a strong and solid scientific capability, especially in our many centers of advanced education. . . .
>
> To the fullest extent compatible with their primary interests in specific fields of science, their basic statutes, and their needs for research results of high quality, all Federal agencies should act so as to:
>
>   a. Encourage the maintenance of outstanding quality in science and science education in those universities where it exists;

* See appendix, pp. 109-16.

b. Provide research funds to academic institutions under conditions affording them the opportunity to improve and extend their programs for research and science education and to develop the potentialities for high quality research of groups and individuals, including capable younger faculty members;

c. Contribute to the improvement of potentially strong universities through measures such as:

—Giving consideration, where research capability of comparable quality exists, to awarding grants and contracts to institutions not now heavily engaged in Federal research programs;

—Assisting such institutions or parts of institutions in strengthening themselves while performing research relevant to agency missions, by such means as establishing university-administered programs in specialized areas relevant to the missions of the agencies.

The President has asked, therefore, that the 1.3 billion dollars we spend in universities directly and the half billion dollars a year we spend on research institutions attached to universities be used to improve higher education and the higher educational system of the country in the course of procuring research. You may well ask what practical impact this is likely to have on the universities. The question is not easy to answer yet. A committee of the Federal Council of Science and Technology, under the chairmanship of Leland Haworth, is reviewing the practices of the various agencies and will make recommendations for steps to implement the President's instruction.

Still, certain things seem clear. In the first place, we do not intend to abandon either the merit system, our general concern for the quality of what is undertaken, or our use of the project system as a base for supporting scientific research. Nevertheless, it seems very likely that more funds will be expended in ways which increase the flexibility of administration, at least in those institutions where capable scientific administration has been developed. I have in mind such programs as the sustaining university grants of the National Aeronautics and Space Administration, the variety of training grants, area grants, and programmatic grants of the NIH, and the institutional grants of the NSF. Some other mechanisms for flexibility may be developed, including perhaps transfers of funds between projects within reasonable limits, or the use of project funds to support central services, for example.

Still another effect will be a more conscious effort to encourage developing institutions, developing departments within institutions, or strong research groups in institutions not yet strong, to grow in areas of the country which are not so well served by advanced educational institutions as others. Of course, the planning and the initiative for development must come from the universities themselves. Federal money cannot buy or create excellence. It can back excellence with funds, and increasingly it can assist institutions with sound plans on the way to excellence. Certainly the quality of the educational institutions in the Research Triangle area of North Carolina was a large factor in persuading the government to establish the Environmental Health Center there.

More and more often, too, the directions of university development will be affected by the location of research facilities and equipment. Since one of the characteristics of many areas in modern scientific advance is the necessity to provide bigger and more expensive special equipment if work is to be undertaken at all, it becomes increasingly impossible to provide such equipment at every university in the country. Thus, it seems likely that the day when every university can aspire to be at the forefront of all fields of modern science is nearly at an end. I think, therefore, that we will see the development of a variety of cooperative arrangements to cope with this difficulty. In high-energy physics this problem has been attacked through the concept of user groups, by which national facilities are available to groups all over the country who carry out the analysis of records and their interpretation at their home sites, but either perform experiments at the national centers or receive raw material from experiments there for work. More generally, several associations of universities which are geographically proximate are now being formed in which each can contribute to the strength of the other by maintaining special facilities which are available to all of the associating universities.

One problem to which I must make reference, but for which I cannot make predictions, is that everywhere there is concern with the plight of the small college and its role in the future. The problems are clear: the small colleges have trouble recruiting faculties in the sciences, and they have difficulties in providing the kind of facilities and the awareness of current change in science which is important if they are to continue to play the strong role that they have in the past. There are some indications that their role may be declining. I am sure that increased federal attention will be focused on this area through programs in various agencies, but I cannot now predict their form.

I have mentioned earlier the trend toward more general-purpose support. Examples of such programs in science might include the traineeship programs of the NIH and NSF, the various facilities programs and equipment programs, the general research grants of the NIH for medical schools, and the institutional grants of the NSF. What is new is the assistance being provided to universities in all fields of study by the Office of Education as the result of several new acts. These include facilities, fellowships, scholarships, loan funds, assistance for libraries, and so on. It seems likely that there will be more.

In closing I want to return to my original theme. The close association of the federal government and the universities in performing many public functions is here to stay. The successful experience we have had so far gives me the greatest confidence that we will continue to develop that association in a way which responds to the needs of all parts of our country and all segments of our population, which places greater responsibility on the university as an institution to plot its course and determine its destiny, and which preserves the freedom of the individual scientist to pursue understanding according to his own insights.

HUGH L. DRYDEN

Deputy Administrator,
*National Aeronautics and Space Administration**

The Role of the University
in the Exploration of Space

I wish to discuss the relationship of science to space exploration, and the role of the university in the exploration of space in the context of its existing relationships with education, research, government, industry, and other elements of our social environment. Then I hope to become provocative in commenting on the future role of the university in the next half century.

The events of the past seven years have had a profound effect on all human affairs throughout the world. Repercussions have been felt in science, industry, education, government, law, ethics, and religion. The toys of our children, the ambitions of our young men and women, the fortunes of industrialists, the careers of military officers, the pronouncements of high church

* On December 2, 1965, shortly after the National Academy of Sciences meeting, Dr. Hugh Dryden died.

officials—all have reflected the influence of the beginning steps in space exploration. No area of human activity or thought, no social institution, has escaped. The university can be no exception.

Those of us who are experiencing the first small steps cannot have the proper perspective to assess the full meaning to the history of man of the crossing of the space frontier. But I believe that its impact must be compared to great developments of past history, such as the Copernican theory which placed the sun, rather than the earth, at the center of our solar system; to the work of Sir Isaac Newton in relating the fall of an apple to the motion of the moon around the earth through the universal law of gravitation; to the industrial revolution; or to other great landmarks in the history of man.

As is well known, scientists view the exploration of space with mixed emotions; but most now realize that it is not an enterprise undertaken by the nation as the next step in the evolutionary development of "big science." Most of our citizens instinctively accept the view stated by the late German space pioneer, Eugene Sänger, in the following terms: "Space flight comes upon us as a natural event born in the deepest depths of the human soul, before which we can only stand humble or defiant; space travel comes upon us whether we love it or hate it or do not heed it at all, whether we believe in it or ridicule it, just as war and high flood tides and death come over us."

The exploration of space does involve what is now called "big science," a stage in the evolution of science which is resisted by many who wish to confine science to the traditions of the last century. The perspective of history shows that science has evolved, has changed, hopefully retaining the valuable characteristics of the past while adapting to a new social environment.

To oversimplify, we have seen the birth of science centuries ago in the work of the natural philosophers. They were usually amateurs, wealthy in their own right or supported by patrons. With insatiable curiosity for knowledge, they could and did study and know all aspects of knowledge then available—the theoretical and the practical—about nature and about man in all his intellectual and spiritual activities. As knowledge expanded, specialization began, and the teacher and his disciples became a community of scholars, an association of specialists, a loose grouping of self-sufficent individuals. With further growth of knowledge and its permanent recording in books and libraries, the number of categories of specialists grew; institutions were built around broader objectives, universities and university departments were invented, and means of interaction between individuals and groups with generally similar interests were organized.

As science grew, the tools of the scientist became more complex and expensive—for example, electron microscopes, infrared spectrometers, computers, and so on—but at first they were operable by the scientist himself or by small groups which included a few technicians. The old traditions of individual freedom and complete control by the scientist were preserved. It merely cost more to support him with adequate equipment. Specialized industries evolved to design, manufacture, and sell the equipment. The days of glass, sealing wax, and wire assemblies created by the scientist himself have largely disappeared.

Then, with the airplane, the accelerators splitting the atom, and the rocket, came big science, involving massive engineering and industrial support, institutes, national laboratories, associations of universities, administration and management of big organizations. All of this was needed to match the more complex needs for further scientific advance, as well as to meet the more important social need of national defense.

On other occasions I have discussed the almost dominant role of the social environment in which the scientist and engineer work and which in most instances seems to be a prerequisite for the intensive development of the scientific concept itself (though not always its discovery), as well as of the ensuing technology. Thus James Maxwell in 1865 and 1873 theoretically described the propagation of electromagnetic waves. Shortly thereafter their existence was demonstrated by Heinrich Hertz (1883), and limited development proceeded. But not until Marconi applied them to signaling in 1895 and succeeded in sending signals across the Atlantic in 1901 were greatly increased resources applied, which were the foundation of large industrial developments resulting in a great social impact.

Today social needs have become much more complex—for example, the war on poverty, the abatement of air and water pollution—and go far beyond the material aspects of our life. The exploration of space may be interpreted as a modern social need which provides the environment to accelerate the growth of science and technology in many cases, not only to develop space capability but also to participate in that complex, dynamic interaction among science, technology, and the social need essential to all. To use an analogy from bacteriology, there has to be a nutrient solution (money and employment opportunities) as well as motivation to feed the scientific and technological effort. Then many latent efforts in science and technology begin to assert themselves and move forward.

One of the major goals of the National Aeronautics and Space Act of 1958 is fundamentally scientific—the expansion of human knowledge of the atmosphere and space; or, in the language of the President's Science Advisory Committee, the exploration of outer space in response to the compelling urge of man to explore and to discover. The sounding rocket, the satellite, and the space probe have made it possible to put instruments in the atmospheric curtain into outer space—near the earth, the moon, and the nearest planets, and probably in a few years to the outer reaches of the solar system—for direct experimental measurements and for an unhampered view of the universe in all wave lengths, from gamma rays to radio waves. Man himself has begun the exploration of nearby space and hopes to reach the moon in a few years. Without the full partnership of scientists, and in particular university scientists, the job would be impossible. In addition, the universities must provide the basic research upon which to build a complex new technology and conduct ground-based experiments which contribute directly to understanding the results of observations in space; they must assist in the conception, design, development, and testing of instruments and space craft; supply the exploratory and basic research necessary to guide the planning and evaluation of scientific missions and experiments in space; and participate as experimenters in space flight missions. Finally, universities are the only knowledge-creating institutions that produce more trained people than they consume, and hence they are the primary producers of scientific manpower.

NASA early decided to rely on the National Academy of Sciences as its primary source of scientific advice through the Academy's Space Science Board. These advisers have contributed immeasurably to whatever credit is due for making space science as excellent as possible under the restraints of "big science," which necessitates a team composed of many more engineers than scientists. Profiting from this advice, NASA has adopted the policy of working within the university structure rather than fostering activities which pull the university researcher away from the teaching environment and of enlisting cooperation in a manner that will not only make it possible for NASA to accomplish its mission but that will also strengthen the university as an institution.

Space science offers completely new methods of attack on some of the oldest and most fundamental problems challenging science, including the structure of the universe, the abundance of the elements in the cosmos, the evolution of the stars and galaxies, the formation of the sun, and the origin of the earth. Extensive exploration has already been carried out in the near-earth region, the upper atmosphere, the ionosphere, and the magnetosphere, and the investigations have been extended into the interplanetary medium beyond the influence of the earth's magnetic field. Extensive attention has been given to the sun, whose activity is responsible for many of the time-dependent phenomena observed in the space near the earth. Observations of the moon and nearer planets have begun. Finally, a beginning has been made on astronomical investigations above the blanketing influence of the earth's atmosphere.

In the missions undertaken primarily for scientific objectives, the choice of launch vehicle, trajectory, and design of space craft are controlled by the scientific requirements, subject to the unavoidable restraints of available resources. The acquisition of fundamental scientific knowledge has top priority. Some missions—such as Ranger and Surveyor—are flown to obtain specific information about the space environment in support of other missions, and although they do give scientific information, their primary motivation is to insure adequate engineering design of space vehicles. In the course of the past seven years, NASA and the universities have learned to adapt to each other's problems, to provide adequate forums and other mechanisms to make possible joint planning of scientific flight missions, and to establish policies which have enabled fruitful cooperation in space science. These have often been reviewed on other occasions and need not be repeated here.

For many years the government mission-oriented agencies have used the resources of the university for research through the project method, a pattern originally developed in most effective form by the Office of Naval Research. A new research contract was developed as a special tool for the support of research at universities, to be awarded largely on the basis of proposals originated by university scientists. This contract, differing markedly from the usual procurement contract, provides a mechanism for tapping the ideas of the entire academic community of scientists, both for the basic research of science and the applied sciences of engineering and medicine.

All the NASA flight misions are undergirded by a program of advanced research and technology, carried out in in-house laboratories of NASA and other government agencies, in universities, and in industry. The work ranges from basic research to applied research and advanced technological development, and there are literally thousands of projects. Among them are projects from the physical sciences, the biological sciences, engineering science, space propulsion technology, vehicle systems technology, space operations technology, tracking, data acquisition and processing, and even a few socio-economic studies.

Mission-oriented agencies support primarily proj-

ects relevant to their mission, although they participate in the general support of basic research. Relevance has been broadly interpreted. For example, in
the field of astronomy, NASA has supported an expansion of ground-based astronomy relating to the moon,
Mars, and Venus, in order to contribute directly to
understanding the results of the early missions to
these celestial objects. It supports the development of
instrumental techniques for measurements from space
vehicles in parts of the spectrum not accessible to
ground-based telescopes, and it supports to a lesser
degree gap-filling projects in basic astronomy in coor-
dination with the National Science Foundation and
other governmental agencies.

In addition to direct project support, a more intimate association is necessary and desirable, as is now
being generally recognized by government and university leaders and by the Congress. Thus in the fiscal
year 1962, NASA initiated a program for utilizing more
fully the present and potential abilities of our universities in the space program. This program included the
encouragement of interdisciplinary groups for research in broad areas, adapted in each case to the interest of the university itself and the needs of NASA;
the provision of research facilities in special cases
where essential to the new activity; and the support of
the training of people in fields relevant to space science and technology through research grants. These
three components—research, facilities, and training—
are complementary, and their relative magnitudes
have been balanced in each case to ensure the most

efficient use of the capabilities and resources provided.

Many of the problems encountered in the space program require an interdisciplinary approach involving the concerted and cooperative efforts of biologists, geologists, physicists, chemists, electronic specialists, metallurgists, engineers, economists, sociologists, and many others. The universities are the only institutions in our society that have the potential ability to bring to bear on our problem such a variety of skills. We have therefore encouraged the integration of related research projects into unified multidisciplinary activities, initiation of new investigations to fill existing gaps, and participation of promising new groups. Thus, able scholars in diverse disciplines are enabled to work together on the broad problems whose solutions resist piecemeal attack.

At many institutions these interdisciplinary activities are seriously impeded by lack of room, and as a consequence NASA has (in special cases in which new programs are being established and where all the circumstances warrant it) helped supply additional facilities, including a building or building additions to provide laboratory space. In many cases this assistance is given in consultation and cooperation with other government agencies as a part of strengthening the university's scientific and technological capabilities, which are available to all government programs.

As a consequence of the report of the Gilliland Committee of the President's Science Advisory Committee, which called for doubling the production of Ph.D.'s in science and engineering by 1970, NASA participated in a government-wide program to attain this goal. Because NASA's appropriation in fiscal 1962, when the program was started, amounted to about one quarter of the federal research and development dollars, NASA took as its ultimate goal the production of one thousand Ph.D.'s annually, which represented approximately one quarter of the increase considered desirable. This program is now nearing the planned level— the entrance of 1,350 new students annually, yielding, after normal attrition, about 1,000 Ph.D.'s at the end of three years for which they may be supported.

Selection of the students and administration of the program are decentralized to the university, the individuals being selected by senior members of the faculty who know the capabilities of the students, who will probably supervise their research training, and who in many cases are directly engaged in research activities supported by NASA. In addition to stipends for the students, funds are made available to help defray the cost of the program to the university. However, these funds are not specifically tied to the students, but are made available to the university with the stipulation that they be used to enhance graduate education in fields relevant to space science and technology. The university itself determines these areas, which include all the fields previously mentioned under the interdisciplinary program. Over 130 universities participate in the training program. There is no commitment that the graduates will work for NASA or the federal government. It is hoped that many will remain at the university. The initial grants, which covered only one hundred students, are just being completed. We have been extremely gratified by the results to date. As of June 15, 1965, we have been notified that Ph.D.'s had been awarded to sixty-eight students. Information is available as to the initial career choice of fifty-eight of these students: forty-four have chosen to remain with the university, thirty-three in research and teaching, and eleven on postdoctoral appointments on Fulbright fellowships; of the remaining fourteen, two entered employment in government laboratories and twelve were engaged by industry.

We turn now to a more debatable and controversial matter—the evolution of the role of the university in the future. We see around us much evidence of the ferment of change in response to what Lloyd Berkner has called a social and economic revolution of a magnitude unprecedented in the history of society and whose roots are nourished by the power of today's science, from which is derived equally powerful technology. It is evident in the invention of new tools of the university organization, such as research institutes within the university but not under departmental control, and associated nonprofit corporations affiliated with a single university or with a group of universities on a regional and, more recently, on a national scale. It is evident in the experiments on the evolution of scientific and, particularly, engineering curricula. It is evident in the demands on university leaders to bring the great resources of the university to bear on the complex social and economic problems of the neighboring community, the region, the nation, and the global community of nations. The university is the one existing social institution where the environment is conducive to scholarship, objective analysis and considered thought, and the interdisciplinary flux of many specialist points of view. No other institution has in one place men skilled in physical science and engineering, in the humanities, in medicine and the life sciences, in sociology and the behavioral sciences, in political science, in law, in theology.

It is not expected that the university will become the primary action agency for solving the economic and social problems of our society or for setting basic social objectives, but it must have a prominent voice and influence. The university should, I think, aspire to intellectual leadership, to observe and analyze, to apply the power of the human mind—that faculty which distinguishes man from animal—to establish a rational basis for policy and action. The direct attack must be undertaken by other institutions, mainly by political agencies. We are now witnessing the evolution of government agencies—particularly those of the federal government—to meet social needs by direct action in all fields, from economics and public health to science and technology. A beginning is being made in the mobilization and integration of the total available resources to attack the most complex social problems.

It is interesting to note the experiments of the state of California in the use of the aerospace industry to survey some of the major problems of urbanization, such as those relating to water resources, sewage and waste disposal, air and water pollution, and transportation. Industry, too, has assembled resources of scientists and engineers and has developed new concepts, such as systems analysis, dealing with the integration and application of knowledge from many fields to complex problems. The aerospace industry has had much experience in adaptation to change and has proceeded somewhat further in its evolution to meet new environments than has the university. In the short span of sixty years (again in an oversimplified view), it has passed through stages somewhat analogous to those traversed by the university over several centuries.

The aerospace industry began with the designer and his apprentices, at a stage where one man knew all there was to be known about the design of airplanes and the underlying science and technology. This was followed by the development of small teams with specialization of effort in aerodynamics, structures, and propulsion. These specialized problems were at first separable, with little interaction between the work of the design specialists. Then aircraft speeds increased, the air flow deformed the structure, the deformation in turn modified the air loads, other interactions occurred, and new specialties, such as vibration and flutter analysis, came into the picture. The aerospace company grew in size and complexity. It became harder to identify a single individual as the designer of its product.

When electronics brought new types of equipment,

such as radar, it was necessary to make design compromises among the diverse requirements of electronics, aerodynamics, structure, and propulsion. Companies with different technologies became associated. Individual companies were expanded into large corporations, with several divisions specializing in the several fields. With the arrival of missiles, atomic weapons, and space vehicles, research groups were established within the aerospace corporation, first made up of engineers and applied scientists, later including basic research scientists in the life sciences as well as the physical sciences. The development task became one of dealing with many systems, subsystems, and components, integrating them with extension of the systems concept to include all aspects of design, construction, and use. Even field maintenance, training of operators, and consideration of the real objectives and values of the whole development enterprise became an activity of the corporation. As the scope and size of projects became very large, even corporations had to be associated to provide the required resources.

In the space program it has been necessary to go still further, to assemble a combined team of industry, government, and university, comprising hundreds of thousands of persons contributing to a single objective. Relations between supplier and customer have grown to an intimate partnership. New institutions, such as the Communications Satellite Corporation, have been invented, and others will undoubtedly follow. The university must be equally flexible and adaptive to meet its responsibilities and opportunities in the next century. Where does this leave the dynamic quality of science, the traditional values of pursuit of excellence, freedom of inquiry, preservation of creativity, and the support of the unconventional new ideas, particularly those of the young scientists? We must be concerned to preserve these essential freedoms which have led to progress of the university in the past.

Paradoxical as it may seem, I believe that these values may not only be preserved but may even be strengthened within the larger framework of increased scope which can provide a sounder human motivation, bring allocation of more resources, provide the satisfaction of great accomplishment in terms of human goals, and a sense of a community of interest with all mankind. Presently, in the exploration of space, there is a free association of individuals, each with complete freedom of individual choice, in the largest and most challenging venture of man, the search for the knowledge of his environment and the application of this knowledge to his benefit. In this group of several hundred thousand people are innumerable examples of the pursuit of excellence, from the renewed pride of the workman in his handicraft, to the intellectual effort of the scientist to analyze and observe. They are mainly young men, unafraid of large problems or rapid change. The unconventional idea is being given attention. The university and the university scientist must and will adapt to the age of space exploration.

LELAND J. HAWORTH

Director, National Science Foundation

Some Problems and Trends
in the Support of Academic Science

Perhaps I can introduce the subject of my remarks by giving a few of what the television people sometimes call headline bulletins.

Latest NSF estimates predict that because of a sharp drop in commitments for research and development facilities total federal funds for research and development in fiscal year 1966 may decline slightly below the figure for 1965. The largest single component—development—will remain essentially constant. But support for basic research is expected to rise about 13 per cent and that for applied research about 10 per cent.

Whereas federal support for research and development has approximately doubled since 1960—from $8.1 billion to $16.1 billion—appropriations for the Office of Education have increased about sevenfold over the same period—reaching a level about $3 billion in the current fiscal year. The Higher Education Act of 1965 will expand still further the support of the federal government to our colleges and universities.

In the recent hearings held by the House Subcommittee on Research and Development, chaired by Congressman Emilio Daddario, the most recurrent substantive questions related to the distribution of federal funds among academic institutions and among geographic regions; to the impact of those funds on the education process; and to the adequacy or inadequacy of the National Science Foundation's support of the social sciences.

On September 13, 1965, President Johnson issued his memorandum to the heads of departments and agencies entitled "Strengthening Academic Capability for Science Throughout the Nation." On September 29 he signed into law the act establishing a National Foundation for the Arts and Humanities, which in his words "will have an unprecedented effect on the arts and humanities of our great Nation."

These examples of recent developments in Washington are generally familiar to all of you, but collectively they have a particular significance for everyone associated with science and science education in our colleges and universities. It is in the context of this significance that I would like to develop my remarks.

Since the war, science has become a magic word. It has enjoyed unprecedented and rapidly growing federal support. Initially this support was primarily directed at immediate exploitation of the practical fruits of science. But increasingly it has been recognized that continuance and growth of those fruits can occur only if the tree that bears them—science itself—is helped to grow and flourish. This more recent trend is illustrated by the statistics I gave earlier. Over a longer period it is shown by the fact that whereas from fiscal year 1960 through fiscal year 1966 federal obligations for development will have appreciably less than doubled, support for basic research will have more than trebled.

Although recognizing a variety of motives, I believe the federal government, especially the Congress, has justified this vigorous support mostly as the means to particular ends. The so-called mission-oriented agencies support science in our institutions of higher education mostly because they were, and are, the best places to have good research done. And while federal officials and the Congress have always acknowledged the value of science as an intellectual and cultural pursuit and that to excel in these pursuits is itself a highly worthwhile goal, with a few exceptions this recognition had in the past only secondary impact on budgets and appropriations.

Similarly, the support of science education was primarily motivated by the desire to provide for the growing and long-range manpower needs in the scientific and engineering fields, in order to enhance our ability to achieve our practical national goals. This attitude is illustrated by the fact that the major federal education action of the 1950's was named the *National Defense* Educational Act of 1958. Even most of the education activities of the National Science Foundation are justified under our act as means to increase research potential.

In a different context congressional concern over what has come to be called "geographic distribution" of federal support of research and development had its origins mostly in the desire to more nearly equalize the economic impact of the support, partly because of the funds as such but more especially, because of the (often exaggerated) effect the activities would have on industrial and other economic growth in the regions that would gain by a wider distribution. Strong academic as well as industrial research centers were desired in no small measure for this reason.

I admit that I have greatly oversimplified; that many among the public and within the government—in both the executive and the legislative branches--took a broader view. But the most driving widespread motives were, in my opinion, practical in nature: Direct attacks toward meeting national goals in defense, in health, in exploitation of natural resources, in industrial development; basic research, much of it at universities, to provide the underlying knowledge needed for achievement of these goals; science education to provide an adequate flow of new, highly-trained scientists and engineers who would carry out both the practical and the more basic work; and, in more recent times, a growing desire among the various regions of the country to share in the economic benefits deriving from the intensive activities supported in all these programs.

But times have been changing at an accelerating pace in the last half dozen years. Without any diminution in the earlier objectives in science and science education, the concept of federal support has been extended to the arts and the humanities, and, after long hesitation, has been accepted across the board in education. Various facets of these changes are worthy of special mention.

The most dramatic and most rapidly progressing change is, of course, that in the support of education. And here there are two impelling motives. The first results from recognition that a highly educated people makes the nation strong in a composite sense; that for our national well-being we must develop the highest competence in all fields of endeavor; and that to achieve this we must have high quality education at every level. Secondly, and importantly, federal policy has evolved in the direction of stronger emphasis on the democratic principle that every citizen is entitled to an opportunity for the best education he has the capacity to absorb effectively—in the field that he wishes to pursue.

There is nothing new in principle in these developments, so far as national philosophy is concerned. Public support of education for both these motives goes back to colonial times. What is new is the realization that with the modern structure of society the federal government must share responsibility for the attainment of the goals.

This trend is accompanied, though as yet in less full and evident fashion, by an increasing acceptance of the value of scholarship and intellectual activity, not merely for potential material rewards, but for their role in fulfillment of the human personality and the development of the human intellect. The attitudes in Congress and the Executive Branch, the Arts and Humanities Foundation Act, the Beautification Program, the President's Memorandum are all symptoms of these trends. To give a striking example of attitudes and interests, a few months ago I watched a congressional subcommittee sit spellbound for thirty or forty minutes while Philip Handler spoke to them of progress in basic science—of Quasers and Quarks, of biochemistry and neural physiology, of progress in understanding life. And no one asked, "Of what use is it?" The subjects were interesting in their own right.

Clearly, the changes in Washington reflect and, indeed, are part of interests developing throughout the country. Certainly there is a pervasive mood to improve education at every level. And the general interest extends higher up the educational ladder than ever before. The general desire to improve, not merely to expand the colleges and universities, including the graduate level, is reminiscent of similar feelings about the high schools that began a generation or so ago. Public support of higher education is growing everywhere—in northeastern states that had only nominal public systems until fairly recently, in the South and the Southwest—indeed everywhere, including those regions of the country that have long supported it well. Rising universities everywhere are striving toward high quality in a way that many of them have never done before and with public sympathy and support such as they have never enjoyed before.

Political leaders recognize and support these public desires. At the state level, governors and legislatures are providing funds, are increasing salary scales, are honoring research and scholarship more and more, as well as providing quantitatively for increasing student bodies. It is now widely recognized that a strong university is a local, state, and regional asset, not only for the opportunities it provides its students but also for its impact on education at all levels, for its ability to attract and hold intellectual and other leaders to the community at large, and for many other reasons. This realization has taken strong root among members of the Congress. Indeed, in my opinion it is now the *strongest* motive in their desire to have what they consider adequate geographic distribution of federal support of academic research and education. To the credit of large numbers of these men, they are willing to think regionally, not merely state by state and district by district. It is increasingly recognized that the beneficial effects of a great educational center extend far beyond its own immediate locale.

What is to be the effect of all this on federal support of science, and what specifically is to be the effect on the role of the National Science Foundation? University science is unprecedentedly healthy. It will not suffer by sharing the spotlight of federal support with other branches of scholarship. Indeed, science can be expected to prosper all the more as the climate of scholarship in general improves. Government commitment to support of academic science in pursuit of ultimate tangible applications is undiminished, and while there may be shifts of emphasis or modifications in the level of support of this type, I see no reason to anticipate any change in basic policy. Support of science for its own sake will, I believe, increase. In keeping with the President's memorandum of September 13, greater care will be taken to distribute the support of academic science in ways so that, without diminishing the quality of research results, the university system will be strengthened.

So far as the National Science Foundation is concerned, we have already been re-examining our role and our attitudes. The new circumstances have accelerated the pace of trends already in motion within the Foundation's activities, and we must seek out fresh approaches to some problem areas. At the same time, the change in climate tends to solidify my view of what I believe to be the role of the Foundation in its relationship with the scientific community.

Before going into that, I should remind you that about a year ago, during preparation of the fiscal year 1960 federal budget, President Johnson adopted a proposal that the National Science Foundation budget be adjusted upward in an attempt to assure that federal support for research in the universities be increased by approximately 15 per cent over that of the previous year to cover the increase in population at the graduate level and the increased cost of research.

While the congressional action on our appropriations request somewhat blunted that particular effort,

Leland J. Haworth

I think the over-all federal position on education and on academic research is reflected well in the President's memorandum of September 13. To quote it briefly:

> In building our national educational system, we must bear in mind all of the parts, and all of the levels— from Head Start for preschool children to the most advanced university levels. At the apex of this educational pyramid, resting on the essential foundation provided for the lower levels, is the vital top segment where education and research become inseparable.

A later paragraph continues in this vein:

> The strength of the research and development programs of the major agencies, and hence their ability to meet national needs, depends heavily upon the total strength of our university system. Research supported to further agency missions should be administered not only with a view to producing specific results, but also with a view to strengthening academic institutions and increasing the number of institutions capable of performing research of high quality.

Still further along in the memorandum, mention is made of the function and responsibilities of the National Science Foundation. "The National Science Foundation continues to have responsibility for augmenting the research capabilities of academic institutions in all fields of science through the support of basic research and research facilities and through measures for improving the quality of education in the sciences."

The National Science Foundation has already been doing many things that are in conformity with the new climate and with the spirit of the Presidential memorandum. No drastically new charter is needed for the Foundation to fit itself comfortably into the changing pattern and direction of support for science and science education. Because of the breadth and flexibility of its mandate, the Foundation is equipped, within limits, to support research and education for the dual purpose of promoting scientific productivity and providing an opportunity for increased cultural and intellectual development for larger numbers of people. At the same time, but with perhaps less immediate impact, Foundation activities can both foster and shelter the image of science as a field of intellectual activity that is worth while for its own intrinsic sake.

For this reason, I believe that the Foundation should be regarded, and should think of itself, as the repository for federal recognition of science as a national resource—a renewable resource that is vital to the national interest. In addition, the Foundation should be the champion and protector of basic research—the fountainhead of new ideas and the area most likely to suffer in a period of economic retooling of support.

By this last I do not mean that the Foundation can assume the function of backstopping every change in pace by other federal agencies, nor should it assume responsibility for doing all the things that others are disinclined to do. On the contrary, aided by the scientific community the Foundation should assess the total needs, should take advantage of all support provided by other agencies and build upon it when appropriate by—to use the President's words again—"augmenting the research capabilities of academic institutions in all fields of science . . . and improving the quality of education." It is in the exercise of leadership and in providing a voice for science in the federal government that the Foundation can make a most significant contribution to the health of academic science.

I would like now to look more specifically at where we have been and are going and examine some of the things that have yet to be done.

First let me say that we must continue our programs in which quality is the overriding criterion. The project system, in which selectivity is based on "judgment by the peers," will continue to be the backbone of our research support. Any changes in this system will be in the direction of grouping into larger packages, and of allowing more flexibility within the university as to how the funds are spent in order to give more opportunity to younger members of the faculty and to cover costs not assignable to single projects. But the methods and criteria for selecting what work will be supported will remain essentially unchanged. Our dedication to the project system is shown by the fact that whereas our total budgetary increase this year over last is 15 per cent, the item for basic research project grants increased 33 per cent.

Similarly, I believe there should continue to be a substantial fellowship program based on a national competition with ability as the sole criterion for awards and with the choice of institution left to the awardee.

Such programs will continue, in the words of the

President's memorandum, "to encourage the maintenance of outstanding quality in science and science
education in those universities where it exists." They
in turn will set the tone of the total effort—will establish goals for others to strive for.

But there is also need to encourage and promote the
pursuit of excellence at additional places. For this reason the National Science Foundation has initiated efforts aimed at supporting those institutions with the
potential for over-all development beyond the standards of conventional competence, or with departmental pockets of strength worthy of cultivation.
Programs aimed at these objectives, which will undoubtedly continue to expand, will as heretofore be in
a separate category from those aimed at present quality, for it would be a serious mistake to try to make
individual decisions by trying to compare present high
quality with potential for improvement as criteria for
choice. So far as I can see, such development programs
will continue to be primarily at the level of the institution, or a unit within the institution, rather than at
the level of the individual scientist.

There has, of course, been recognized for some
years the need for more really good first-class universities among our institutions of higher education. This
was highlighted in the Seaborg Report issued by the
President's Science Advisory Committee in 1960. Emphasis at that time was on the objective of more strong
universities in order to have stronger science both in
the sense of direct research results and in the sense of
educating talented scientists and engineers. This

is still a major objective, but added to that is the necessity not only for strengthening science nationally but also for providing more first-class educational opportunities for our young people. The goal now has a fuller and more symmetrical appearance. Federal support of science is intended to make science strong, and science education stronger in parallel. We must continue in this direction, but we must also consider the opportunity offered to the individual as a part of the structure we are seeking to improve.

Fortunately, the evolution of our institutions of higher education has, in recent years, developed a number of very promising institutions which are beginning to offer real competition to the traditional leaders. The Science Development Program, announced in 1964, has the primary purpose of providing a major boost for such institutions. To date the Foundation has announced ten grants of this type for a total value of some $35 million. They cover a multitude of purposes—faculty improvement and expansion, purchase of equipment, provision of laboratory space, establishment of interdisciplinary programs, and so on.

There are other promising institutions, both four-year colleges and universities, which need a kind of boost based on criteria different from those applying to the Science Development Program. We are planning and will soon announce an extension of this program which will attempt to bolster existing strength in specific fields at institutions which we cannot now support more broadly in the parent program. We hope and believe that departmental islands of strength can, if properly supported, serve as centers around which the universities can build further strength in other departments.

Another of the newer mechanisms I might mention is the Graduate Traineeship Program, which was also initiated in fiscal year 1964, with the objective of expanding graduate populations by exploiting hitherto unused capacities in many of our universities. Under this program, the institution applies for the number of traineeships it believes it needs in the various eligible fields of science. Grants are awarded on the basis of departmental merit and capacity for student expansion. Ultimate selection of individual recipients of awards is made by the institution at the local level. In its first year of operation traineeships were limited to the engineering fields. Last year the program was expanded to include mathematics and the physical sciences, grants being given to some 160 universities. In the coming year it will be further expanded to include biology and the social sciences, with a total of forty-one hundred traineeships awarded. One important aspect of the traineeship program is its developmental effect. It gives the institution an opportunity to attract more good graduate students, and this aspect will assume greater importance as the program expands to reach the needs of more graduate students. With the maturing of the traineeship program we are phasing out the cooperative fellowship program, using the funds to increase the numbers of both the traineeships and the regular graduate fellowships.

Also developmental in nature is our program of institutional base grants designed to give flexible support and related to research support at the various institutions by a tapered formula which favors those getting the least amount of support for specific purposes. On the average, the flexible funds are about 8 or 10 per cent of the base amount.

The National Science Foundation has long been active in undergraduate and especially precollege education in the sciences. The trends of the times call for more intensive and extensive federal support in these areas—bearing in mind the need for greater equality of opportunity. The President's memorandum reaffirms the Foundation's responsibilities, especially in the institutions of higher learning.

There is much that needs to be done to improve undergradute teaching. Let me say, first, however, that in general I hold little or no brief for the allegation that federal support of research has detracted seriously from undergraduate teaching. I dispute the contention heard in some quarters that certain of our major universities have become giant research factories concentrating on federally sponsored projects to the detriment of their educational functions.

But there are difficulties. The good teacher must be a scholar. And research is an important form of scholarship, although by no means the only one. The good teacher must be alive to his field; he must keep up with its contemporary advances, and no better mechanism for this exists than to be actively contributing to advances. Perhaps the time spent on research and on graduate and other advanced students does not permit the faculty as a whole to devote all desirable attention to the elementary students. But this is because the faculties are too few in numbers. And this is not a new phenomenon.

I would like to repeat for you the remark of a young chemistry student which recently came to my attention. These are his words: "You cannot imagine what a crowd of people come to these lectures. The room is immense, and always quite full. We have to be there half an hour before the time to get a good place, as you would in a theater; there is also a great deal of applause; there are always six or seven hundred people." The quotation is taken from a letter written by Louis Pasteur about 125 years ago in which he describes the chemistry lecture at the Sorbonne.

Another factor bearing on this criticism of our larger universities can be found in the surviving vestiges of what was at one time the conventional popular view of what constitutes a college education. Like so many other things in our times, the nature of undergraduate education has changed. It is no longer a passive experience in which attendance at lectures will suffice, and it is sometimes a shock for the students to discover that it is not an extension of the sheltered high school environment. At a significant number of institutions higher education has become a serious and demanding challenge calling for vigorous independent study. There is no longer room for the dilettante or the academic passenger—for Joe College with his raccoon coat and ukelele, who boasted that he "never cracked a book."

However, I do not feel that this criticism can be

completely shrugged off. Nor do I feel any sense of complacency about the status of undergraduate science education in our academic institutions as a whole. Many people feel that, especially in some of the larger institutions, elementary science courses are viewed as elimination contests, a method for separating the men from the boys before the former get on with the serious business of pursuing careers in science. Perhaps more thought and care to present the subjects in such a way as to inspire interest in the subject and to give the student better opportunity to appreciate and understand its deeper meanings would both improve the progress of those who do continue and would also prove useful in the more general sense to those who cannot or do not wish to pursue such careers.

In any case there is much room for improvement in undergraduate science curricula in most of our institutions. Especially in the four-year colleges there is a serious problem of recruiting and retaining adequate members of the faculty, and enabling them to keep pace with the progress of science. And about 40 per cent of all our science majors come from institutions that do not grant the Ph.D. degree. Undoubtedly, with more adequate programs the number would be augmented.

The Foundation has several modest programs to assist in improving undergraduate education—curriculum improvement projects, science faculty fellowships, undergraduate research participation programs, sponsorship of summer institutes and faculty exchange relationships, and so on. The Office of Education will, of course, also support many such endeavors. But much more needs to be done.

I believe the Foundation should take as its first priority what might be called the research and development of science education—supporting experimentation and innovation in teaching methods and the development of teaching materials. So far as we are able we should support the efforts of individual institutions to improve their faculties and other aspects of their local situations. Cooperative arrangements between institutions should be encouraged. But any large-scale support for what might be called the direct operational problems of the many institutions would take substantial augmentations of our budgets. I am sure that the federal government will eventually embark upon such large-scale ventures, but what will be the relative responsibilities of the Foundation and the Office of Education is not yet determined.

Here I would like to state my opinion that more than ever in the national interest the universities must take the leadership in our whole education process. I think the kind of parochialism that once led some institutions to regard themselves as islands of scholarship detached from the rest of our society is fading, and more of our leaders are recognizing that they must help the colleges as well as help themselves to educate future generations of college students.

According to any reasonable standard, we have today too few well-prepared and stimulating teachers at all levels of education. The situation may well become worse before it improves. In any case, it is my view that the universities have a special responsibility to try to do the best job they can in motivating able students toward careers in teaching, to make sure the education they receive fits them as fully as possible for the teaching roles they are to play, and to assist them in future years to keep abreast of the changing face of science. Interinstitutional arrangements between universities and colleges can help in this and many other ways.

Now let me return to my general theme—the growing interest in scholarship in all areas and in improving and extending all our institutions of higher learning. The scientific community has played an important role in bringing this about. Its attainments, visible as they are to the public eye, have demonstrated for all to see the public and individual values of intellectual progress and of higher education. But for the example of the National Science Foundation, there would not be one for the arts and the humanities. The example set by federal support of education in the name of science has been an enormous factor in dispelling the long-prevailing fears of the bugaboos of federal control of the education process.

Our reward will be a better intellectual and scholarly climate in the country as a whole—one in which science itself can flourish even more.

We should be optimistic and we should be proud.

JAMES A. SHANNON
Director, National Institutes of Health

Biomedical Sciences—
Present Status and Problems

Tʜᴇ impact of growth of the biomedical sciences, particularly over the past decade, may necessitate major changes in institutional forms. A brief review of the development of these sciences will help explain the need and define the shape and direction of future programs.

In 1940 those portions of science relevant to the understanding of disease served as a base for the categorical structure of the National Institutes of Health. In the latter part of the forties and the early fifties, they further served as the base for support of a nationwide effort against all the major health problems. In the 1950's the thrust of the forties was to continue, but changes in the scientific base occurred. There began to emerge, in a highly purposeful way, an understanding of the molecular dynamics of biological phenomena, an application of physical sciences and mathematics as disciplines capable of far-reaching

61

contributions, a shaping and refinement of behavioral studies to a point where the term "science" was now warranted, and a group of studies aimed at the broad problems of human development.

As we survey the sixties, there comes to attention a searching inquiry as to what was wrought in the past two decades. Where are we now and where are we going? This inquiry can be fruitful, but it should not only probe the present scene and assure its continuation in the future; it should also look quite freely for new devices, new mechanisms, and new basic activities that are more suited for the next twenty years than a simple persistence of the habits developed up to the present time.

Today the field of biomedical science is characterized largely by undifferentiated effort through the support of individual scientists. There is still a multiplicity of disease problems, very few of the major ones having been resolved over the past twenty years. Many scientists have withdrawn from the study of disease as such, and an understandable and valid concept of science for science's sake has emerged. But this is not healthy if it implies a retreat from problems that must be attacked for a variety of social reasons And indeed, in addition to the spectrum of diseases that remain prevalent and devastating, we have identified new areas demanding attention. Consider, for example, the study of the biological, behavioral, and intellectual development of the child as an end in itself, with a view to coping ultimately with mental retardation and assuring healthy intellectual growth.

Here, we are beginning to explore environmental factors with a wholly new social orientation.

Our national program in support of science is entering a phase in which the decision whether to support a given field depends less upon technical considerations than upon social need. If we are to continue to have adequate support for the fundamental as well as the applied (and for strictly applied research as opposed to developmental engineering), then the aggregate effort must be to develop some sense of balance between the two approaches. Take, for example, the problem of water pollution, which has long since ceased to challenge the medical investigator. Water pollution, beyond a doubt, will yield to techniques of management—to an approach that relates the capacity of the nation's water resources to the ways in which we use them. The field of air pollution affords a comparable case. We certainly inhale numerous carcinogens in perhaps dangerous amounts, not only from cigarettes but from a wide variety of hydrocarbon wastes; but knowledge of these carcinogens does not provide the thrust for their elimination nearly so much as the social pressure of people living within our metropolitan areas who insist on clean air as essential for comfort. Or again, a modern agricultural industry has introduced into our daily diet an array of potent chemical agents, many of which have been inadequately assessed. Here, a sufficient public clamor could provide the impetus for corrective measures, including the necessary scientific investigation.

Such complex problems as these must be considered

with a view to their orderly exploration. This exploration, at whatever level it is undertaken, does not always coincide with the neat departmental structure of our universities and professional schools. These organizations, developed first for undergraduate education and later modified to provide discipline-oriented training for the predoctoral student, more or less tend to perpetuate themselves in the image of their forebears. An examination of our academic enterprise, whether cursory or in depth, reveals an absence of institutional design to provide meaningful acquisition or utilization of the far-ranging new knowledge that will be necessary to meet paramount social needs. This, indeed, posits a critical situation confronting the scientist on the one hand and the public administrator on the other.

Most federal agencies have social purposes. The defense department provides for the physical protection of our national security; the agriculture agency is responsible for a sound source of high-quality food and effective handling of a wider range of agricultural products, including fibers, woods, and the like; and the public health branch strives to ensure buoyant health, emotional stability, and optimal intellectual growth. Up to the present time, it has fortunately been possible, in accepting these social missions, to convince the Congress and through them the American people that the setting of priorities, the selection of fields, the development of terms and conditions of support must be left in the hands of scientists if the work is to be done on a productive level. The setting of social goals is probably not the scientist's role. If he chooses, however, to operate within a frame of reference that has certain goals, then he will surely be influenced by them.

Medicine must provide the biomedical sciences with institutional forms that permit the realistic isolation of reasonable technical and scientific objectives. It must support work toward those objectives in a form flexible enough to contribute to the strength of independent imaginative activity while yielding practical scientific advances. Providing support for the independent scientist is a simple matter, and all of the agencies that have undertaken to do so over the past ten or twenty years have succeeded. But establishing a system of support that capitalizes on progress and directs itself to attainable goals is quite difficult. The biomedical scientist in general has the intellectual capability to produce needed and useful knowledge, but he usually does not have control of all the necessary resources. By contrast, the federal administrator, exhorted by Congress to activate the array of scientific disciplines required to meet an objective, may find the individual scientist apathetic toward participating in a group effort that places little premium on either his capability or the goals he perceives as important. And yet, in the face of this conflict, society demands that biomedical enterprise in the aggregate be a socially purposeful one. This is the problem.

We are quite a long way toward the solution of that problem, acknowledging and sustaining, as in the past, the drive of the individual investigator for scientific progress and simultaneously providing an environment where his efforts, together with those of his related colleagues, can be more socially focused. This can be accomplished in a way that will tend to strengthen rather than weaken a somewhat changed university. The simplest solution may be to permit in selected areas the progressive build-up of quasi-research institutes ("quasi" because I do not refer to free-standing research institutes, external to our universities) with the university system of graduate education. These would serve as resources for professional education without depending upon their contribution to it as the basis of support.

Such institutes are viewed by some with concern, by others as being the hopeful way to meet the social need for scientific advances. There is a fair amount of experimentation under way. The Division of Communication Sciences at the Massachusetts Institute of Technology would qualify, and the Institute of Human Genetics at the University of Michigan. There are also the older forms of cancer and cardiovascular institutes, some good, some poor—but the fact that some of these are poor does not necessarily mean they can never be good. Clearly, without some new institutional forms, information essential to the resolution of certain major problems would not be forthcoming, and we therefore have in the process of development a series of institutes motivated by specific, socially desirable biomedical goals. These should be able to build upon the experience of similar endeavors in the past. Institutes of this sort can be constructed and developed within the framework of the institution, and perhaps will flourish to a far greater extent than would be possible with comparable support distributed through the normal disciplines of the university.

The dental sciences provide a good example of a field that needs such attention. The social cost of dental disease is fantastic. There are 50 dental schools now, and it is calculated that in terms of reparative dentistry there should be 160. Since we are not going to have 160 dental schools, the only alternative is to determine the underlying causation of dental disease and prevent it.

For some ten years, however, we have attempted without success to develop dental sciences in significant fashion. We estimate that the dental schools of America have a full-time equivalent of approximately three thousand faculty members. Some eight hundred scientists or their full-time equivalents, including those in dental schools, are applying themselves to dental research. In examining school after school, we could find no "critical mass" of scientists that could sustain work of excellence, and indeed most of the schools had no significant research activity. So we have proposed (and this has been accepted with vigor at six of our stronger universities) the establishment of a full-scale activity in the dental sciences—ranging from morphology and genetics through microbiology, biochemistry, and pathology—in an institute framework. This arrangement, which will set out some major goals and apply the talents necessary to achieve them, will provide a setting where older scientists can replenish and expand their skills, where young scientists can be trained, and where big problems can be attacked.

NIH also proposes the establishment of a limited number of institutes of pharmacology and toxicology. When the idea was presented at a recent meeting of the American Society for Pharmacology and Experimental Therapeutics, opinion was evenly divided. It could be demonstrated, however, that the present departments of pharmacology in large measure have tended to recede from national needs as the medical sciences increased in scope. For example, they were little interested in studying environment contaminants. Thus it becomes necessary here, as with the dental field, to bring an array of energetic young scientists together—biochemists, organic chemists, mathematicians, biologists, and the like—and to provide a setting where individuals can address themselves to their tasks. As an additional incentive, large amounts of necessary repetitive work would be done on contract rather than wholly within the resources of the medically oriented pharmacologist or toxicologist.

In similar fashion, NIH is developing institutes of developmental sciences, which will engage investigators both biologically and behaviorally oriented. Their work will range from experimental embryology through the morphological sciences. They will study the complicated process of human development, beginning prior to conception and continuing through full development of the child, and in the latter phase will require the clinical skills that are commonly available in departments of obstetrics, gynecology, and pediatrics. But the focus will be on development. If left to individual grants within individual departments, this program would miss the necessary interaction of many skills, the advantages of viewing the same phenomena at different levels of biological organization. The integrated approach is literally impossible within the structure of today's universities and medical schools.

Similarly, we are striving to develop a program to study the aging process, approaching both biological and behavioral aspects in a fashion that will be mutually beneficial.

In the fields of dental science, pharmacology-toxicology, human development, and aging, a systematic effort to develop productive research within the con ventional limits of the ordinary departmental structure has met with a notable lack of success. We are therefore developing these new institutional forms in a way that utilizes their potentialities rather than repeating the pattern that has been criticized elsewhere. This approach will involve research on a very broad front. The individual scientist will be able to operate effectively and need not feel submerged by the organization from which his support is derived. The program will provide more extensive opportunities for graduate education than are generally available in our graduate departments today, anticipating the need ten years hence. But what is equally important, this aggregate activity will be serving an identifiable and scientific program with a perceptible social goal. This is the institutional device that we are exploring now in great depth, in the four areas mentioned above, with a view to determining whether it is possible to satisfy, on the one hand, the driving needs of young scientists and, on the other, a very real and justifiable public pressure. A final objective is to develop this program in a fashion that will strengthen our total scientific establishment.

Part Two

TWO VIEWS FROM THE UNIVERSITY

CHARLES E. ODEGAARD

President, University of Washington

Humanistic Aspects of Science

W<small>HAT</small> I have on my mind is large, complex, and confusing, but I shall nonetheless proceed because I am convinced that the object of my concern is important. If I expose it to you, confused as it may be, perhaps it will appear that you will share my concern and will help find the necessary remedies.

This concern I have is not new. It began to take shape tangibly in connection with my own personal efforts on the eve of World War II to teach medieval intellectual and religious history in what could be called the secularized environment of a modern university. I shared then—as I respect it still—the scholar's zest for the hunt, the conviction that the researching is itself an end to be prized, the conclusion that knowledge is its own reward. So it was to me; and so I tried to stir up in my students a similar scholarly appetite for inquiry, in this case into the religious and intellectual thought and attitudes of medieval men. I experienced the teacher's joy in seeing some respond, but I had to admit to myself that I was disturbed by the number of those I left untouched by my contagion. I am not talking about proselyting apprentices for commitment to careers as medieval historians. I am talking only about the lack of response of students in terms of interest in and curiosity about the Middle Ages—and this from students whom I could not dismiss in my mind as either unintelligent or stupid. I am talking about students who either said or implied, "Why bother with this knowledge?" Clearly they were not yet ready to commit themselves to the hunt—at least in my medieval direction—without more reason than the zest for the hunt.

My sense of failure drove me to pedagogical experimentation until one day in my fumbling I discovered something about teaching history, something which may seem painfully obvious and which no one had ever told me. To put it in a nutshell, history should be taught not by beginning at the beginning but backwards, from the present to the past. I found that I made more inroads on the indifference of disinterested students as I experimented in my course by beginning not, for example, with an analysis of Augustine but with a request to my students to state some proposition in which they believed, some value, whatever that might be, which they held. After they had recovered from what some regarded, even if they did not say so, as sheer impertinence on the part of an instructor who had no business prying into their personal affairs, a few students would begin to volunteer some affirmations, often value propositions with which at

least some of their colleagues could identify. Despite
a certain amount of stumbling, I could ultimately relate this contemporary affirmation about the human
condition to what medieval men had thought and said
and done about similar matters. Students began then
to converse with me and their fellows about the ideas
of Augustine and Gregory, Francis and Thomas; and
we were off to a study of history which was, I trust,
scientific in its respect for modern historical method
and—in a crude and faltering way—humanistically
relevant. Here then was an intimation that knowledge
—even of such a recherché aspect of the universe of
human experience as the Middle Ages—could be both
a rewarding investigation for those curious about the
past of mankind and also meaningful in dealing with
the active present of the student.

Subsequently, four years of World War II spent in
the Navy, mostly at sea, far from academic life, where
I was exposed to men of most diverse backgrounds,
drove me to a great sense of the underlying preoccupation of many men with the direction and purposes of
the human condition and to a greater awareness of
their hunger to feel themselves involved as individuals
in some kind of a context with the universe, however
partial and fragmentary. My encounter with men under tension brought to the surface of my conscious-
ness more awareness of the pressure on individual
lives from the entanglement of purposes in life, however unarticulated and inchoate these may be.

Then I returned from these war years to participate
in various roles in the life of a university world which,

in response to challenges I need not recapitulate here, has demonstrated enormous capacity to extend the fields of knowledge even while it has absorbed vastly more students in its midst. You and I know how compulsively we have labored at our tasks of learning and teaching in these last twenty years. Are we also aware of all the characteristics and the impact of the higher learning as we seek to dispense it?

Despite all the obvious triumphs of science and learning in these last twenty years, we are forcibly made aware of strong voices of dissent coming from a noticeable number of the younger generation, particularly from some bright and articulate university students. The house of intellect is under noisy activist attack from some of the very apprentices we thought we were in process of admitting to membership.

The recent student protest movement is obviously a complex phenomenon, and there may well be as many diagnoses of it as there are diagnosticians. To use an analogy with its inevitable shortcomings, the dissidence of the students may be like a patient's complaint which ranges from a headache to aching legs to a general malaise without a clear focus. It is the task of the diagnostician to try to separate the secondary and tertiary symptoms from the primary ones which suggest the more basic therapeutic procedures needed. At the risk of substantial error I will venture to deal with one major source of this malaise. First let me set aside certain prominent, but I believe secondary, phenomena. Of course, there runs through the student dissent movement a pronounced pitch for power, but I believe that this is largely incidental. Dissatisfied individuals frequently affirm a desire to take over the system, but if they had the power, what would they do? What do they really want? Power can be a means to an end. What is the end they seek?

Obviously there is a demand by the students for what is called more personal contact with faculty, more individual attention; and they make specific reference to mass relationships between faculty and students, to the presence in our institutions of too few teachers, to the indifference to teaching of the senior faculty we do have and to the inexperience of our junior faculty to whom teaching responsibilities are excessively shunted. I will not attempt here to assess the merits of these charges against academe beyond saying that there are great pressures upon the universities today which make it difficult to maintain a rounded sense of proportion in our activities; that academic staffs are confronted by demands for attention from a variety of constituencies in addition to the numerous enrolled students; and that universities today are generally undermanned for the responsibilities they are expected to bear. The university presidents of the last decade yield to no one in the persistence with which they have sought to persuade society at large to provide greater resources for enlarged faculties at our institutions. Let us agree here that there is a problem of inadequate numbers of faculty and that beyond the enlargement of the academic corps much needs to be done in the reassessment of our teaching efforts, especially at the undergraduate level.

But even if we had the enlarged academic corps warranted by the great increase in number of students and even if faculties developed a heightened emphasis on and involvement in teaching responsibilities, I submit that there would still be an unmet complaint from these dissident students. For I think that they want from faculties not merely more conversation but an altered character in the conversation, not only more substance but an altered substance. It is as though they sensed a vitamin deficiency in their educational diet and were trying, however clumsily, to tell us this. For all the expression of rebelliousness against the university "establishment," they are not really running away from us. Indeed, they are still asking us for conversation and attention. The beatnik fringe is not hanging around the railroad yards like hoboes of old, but stays instead on the edges of universities. The extreme dissidents who say that they want to take over the government of universities are not proposing to expel the faculty. It is rather that they want the faculty to converse more with them about something they see in the world with the eyes of youth.

Remember that this youth is in many respects better educated, better informed, more conscious of the world and its global human interrelationships than we were at their age; and they have the courage and forthrightness of youth to try to tell us that they do not sense in our present university conversation with them enough relevance to a world they know exists, a world they are inheriting and concerning which they know they have to make choices, a world which we may think they simplify but about which they feel deeply. Listen to them. They attribute to our generation complaisance with the world, which, as they would put it, our generation has made but which they view as a deeply troubled inheritance. They scorn an acceptance of affluence as a goal or as an achievement; and so they dramatically reject it by demonstrative beatnik hoboism. They are quick to charge us with inactivity in the presence of great moral and social issues against which they counterpose a vigorous activism. In their simplicities they may very well be unfair to the older generation. But it may be easy for us to be unfair to them, all for want of the right kind of conversation with them, a continuing active conversation about values and the moral implication of choices in the human affairs we all confront. In short, are they not trying to suggest to us a want of humanism in our teaching?

This is not a plea for the humanities as disciplines or a justification of the new federal foundation for the humanities and arts, though I have done both with the same zeal, I believe, with which I have sought to help the cause of science and technology. I am talking about the possibility of pursuing knowledge in the sciences as well as in the humanities with a passion for knowing which is matched by a passion for bringing the resultant knowledge to bear on the manifold moral issues and actions concerning which living men day by day are making choices.

Our dissident students may be dupes on occasion, and they are doing a number of unwise things. They overshoot the mark and evidence irrationality and confusion. Let us grant that they still need to learn many lessons. But if this be so, who should be trying to teach them these lessons? The fact remains, I believe, that in their confused way they are reminding us that men are valuing animals confronted by demanding and troublesome choices and that university experience should be brought to bear on this moral responsibility of men. They do not want us to impose a moral code on them. They are quick to reject a ready-made moral suit of armor tailored for them by someone else. But they want us to talk with them about the moral implications of the knowledge we acquire and dispense.

We have lived through a generation which has too often swept the difficult problem of analyzing values and their implications under the rug, presumably either to await definite scientific conclusions which will answer moral questions or make these untidy questionings unnecessary. But meanwhile the pressure of events each day forces all of us to make value decisions now of titanic consequence, and youth increasingly will not be put off to a later day for moralizing.

They are right enough that they are gaining adherents. In its own form of testimony to the growing recognition of the importance of intellectuals and academe to society, *Life* magazine editorialized against "academic ponderousness" and "the stultifying demands of 'scientific method' misapplied." It quotes Gordon Allport's attack on "galloping empiricism" in which he said: "We have too few restraints holding us to the structure of a life as it is lived. We find ourselves confused by our intemperate empiricism which often yields unnamable *[sic]* factors, arbitrary codes, unintelligible interaction effects, and sheer flatulence from our computers."

The intellectual life of the last generation has been marked by a want of attention in universities to living morality as part of the domain of knowledge seeking, a want of attention to current moral issues encouraged by "scientism" run riot, a blight furthered not only by the contemptuous attitude of some scientists toward moral problems because they cannot, or at least have not, been rammed into the relative certitude of test tubes as well as by the dessicating "historicism" of some humanists who pursue mankind's story as though it had no contemporary last chapter.

In a book with the suggestive title, *The Disinherited Mind,* Erich Heller speaks of the scholar's (he is thinking particularly of the literary scholar's) "struggle against bias and prejudice in his own approach and appreciation," but then he asserts that the scholar

> would be ill-advised to concentrate exclusively on those aspects of his discipline which allow the calm neutrality of what is indisputably factual and "objective." His business is, I think, not the avoidance of subjectivity, but its purification; not the shunning of what is disputable, but the cleansing and deepening of the dispute. As a teacher he is involved in a task which would appear impossible by the standards of the scientific laboratory: to teach what, strictly speaking, cannot be taught, but only "caught," like a passion, a vice or a virtue.

Charles E. Odegaard

For years I have sought to comprehend what Alfred North Whitehead really meant when he wrote in the preface of his *Aims of Education,* "The whole book is a protest against dead knowledge, that is to say, against inert ideas." I think he meant to advocate education for a morally sensitive, live, choosing man using the full range of scientific knowledge and ideas available to him to cleanse and deepen his understanding of the disputed choices before him.

Resurgence of the humanistic aspect of teaching in our universities may be dismissed by some as primarily the burden of the humanities, but I cannot in my mind dismiss the possibilities for the revelance of scientific disciplines to man's present choosing. In the realignment of university conversation to intensify its humanistic content the help of scientists as well as humanists is needed. This is why I bring my appeal to you as—in all deference—high priests of science in our land, whose commitment to this task will make it far easier of accomplishment. You and I, scientists and humanists, all have parts to play—if knowledge is to be humanized.

And I make my appeal in all urgency. For now is the time when we as a people are called upon for utmost wisdom. Like it or not as we may, aspire to it or not as we may, the hand of history is writing a chapter on mankind in which we are a people possessed of power, hence an imperial people with the responsibilities such power inevitably entails. Our time is at hand, however humble we might wish to be.

One hundred eleven years ago, three years after the

first white men settled in this city of Seattle, the Indian chief whose name was given to the city spoke to the territorial governor of Washington. I suspect that his remarkable words will touch your inner being. Chief Seattle said to General Isaac Stevens:

> There was a time when our people covered the whole land, as the waves of a wind ruffled sea cover its shell swept floor.
>
> The very dust under your feet responds more lovingly under our footsteps than under yours.
>
> Our dead never forget the beautiful world that gave them being.
>
> Every part of this country is sacred to my people. Now my people are few and resemble the scattered trees of a storm swept plain.
>
> Why should I murmur at the fate of my people? Tribes are made up of individuals and are no better than they are. Men come and go like waves of the sea.
>
> Even the white man whose God walked and talked with him as friend is not exempt from the common destiny. We may be brothers after all. We shall see.

We shall all be brothers in the panoply of history.

The Northwest Ordinance of 1787 affirmed: "Religion, morality, and knowledge being necessary to the good government and welfare of mankind, schools and the means of education shall forever be encouraged." May it be said of you and me that we found the wisdom to serve our schools and means of education in such a way as to further the good government and welfare of mankind and found ultimately a place of honor among our brothers.

PHILIP HANDLER

James B. Duke Professor of Biochemistry,
Duke University

Science and Government—
Opportunities and Conflicts

As the federal budget in support of research and development has grown, it has been subject to ever more intense scrutiny by the Congress, by economists, as well as by scientists themselves. Many in positions of influence have recently suggested that our national effort in fundamental research may have passed its zenith and that the resources of our nation should increasingly be utilized for "practical applied research and development." In reply, a simple recital of the dictum that "Basic research is the most practical activity in which we can engage" is clearly insufficient and less than persuasive. Accordingly, it seems worth while to attempt to develop some appreciation of the accomplishments of present and past research as compared with the prospects which may be envisaged for tomorrow, to relate these to the human condition, and offer some guidelines for those who are responsible for the construction and management of major programs in support of our national research enterprise.

The eight years since the appearance of Sputnik in orbit have been breathtaking. In almost every branch of science American research has forged well ahead of that of all other nations on the globe. We have seen more deeply into the interior of the atomic nucleus and farther out to the edges of space. We have developed a firmer comprehension of that which lies beneath the visible surface of the earth and begun to grasp the magnitude of the task of exploring the ocean depths. In all likelihood, future histories of science will contend that our most notable achievements have been those which have begun to reveal something of the nature of life itself. But, it is my thesis in this discussion that the tasks of fundamental scientific research have only begun.

The essential nature of the atomic nucleus with its confusing array of elementary particles still eludes us. The awesome distance and incredible energy release of quasi-stellar objects have only deepened the mystery of the age and the history of the universe. We have not yet sampled the earth's mantle and know little of the nature of this planet. We are woefully ignorant of the seas—their bottoms, their dynamics, and their inhabitants. The science of chemistry has only recently entered upon a renaissance which may yet illuminate the classical questions of molecular structure and chemical dynamics. These developments must surely contribute to our understanding of the physical universe and contribute enormously to man's future welfare if sufficient opportunity be provided.

Bright as the future of research in the physical sciences must be, the prospects offered by the life sciences appear yet more dazzling. Allow me to present this vision in somewhat greater detail as it is viewed through the eyes of this biochemist.

Prospects in Biological Research

For biology, generally, probably the most important single conclusion reached to date is the conviction that living systems *do* indeed obey the physical and chemical laws that govern the rest of the universe, that the detailed working of the living organism *is* amenable to exploration by physical and chemical probing, and that the properties of living organisms are *totally* comprehensible in chemical terms. To be sure, knowledge of the chemistry of the components of living systems is still inadequate. The catalogue, simply listing such components, is incomplete. Moreover, we have just begun to learn something of the three-dimensional structure of a few of the macromolecules characteristic of living forms, and we can only speculate concerning the rules governing such structures. This must be a major effort for the foreseeable future. Comprehension of life is impossible until the macromolecules which make life possible have been fully described.

For biochemists, the thirties and forties were largely

devoted to elucidation of the mechanisms by which the potential energy of food stuffs is made available, at constant temperature, to the living cell to preserve its high degree of order and permit it to do work against the environment. Thereafter, interest focused on the remarkable, multitudinous chemical transformations by which the materials of the environment are converted into the compounds characteristic of life, that is to say, the processes by which we convert what we eat into what we are. These tasks remain unfinished, but the principles have been established and seem secure. And the information and understanding so derived was an imperative preface to the next chapter, the examination of genetic mechanisms at the molecular level.

It may appear that the study of genetic mechanisms has bathed the innermost secrets of life in a brilliant light for all to see. And indeed, as compared with all the years before, this would certainly appear to be so. Answers to some of the principal questions concerning genetic mechanisms—and this is as close as one can come to the older question, "What is life?"—have been provided in quick succession, and these can be expected to hold the center of the biological stage for several more years. Life has not been synthesized and is not about to be. Nevertheless, these have been immense accomplishments. Already they necessitate an overhaul of our philosophical systems, and of education in science, as well as reconsideration of the social relationships of science and society.

But we have barely entered the Age of Biology; the

most wondrous revelations are yet to come. What has been learned, to date, relates only to the grossest, most obvious manifestations of life, to those structures and functions most readily accessible to our exploration. For example:

It is 165 years since the Academy of the First Republic offered a prize of one kilogram of gold for the best answer to a question which, today, may be translated as, "How *does* an enzyme work?" Although we can offer an answer, in general terms, which would have satisfied those who first posed this question, none of us, today, would be willing to award that prize. The question remains unanswered, even for a single enzyme, and it is clear that there are almost as many answers to the question as there are enzymes.

We have just begun to devise techniques for ascertaining the mechanisms which keep the activities of a single cell tuned as a harmonious whole; those activities reflect the operation within each cell of hundreds of each of several thousand different kinds of enzyme molecules distributed through the cytoplasm and the various subcellular organelles. There is little inkling yet of how this integration is accomplished. We do not understand the factors which determine the number or the distribution of those subcellular organelles. Indeed, several of them appear to come equipped with their own little packages of genetic information as if they were independent foreign bodies which give direction and specificity to their own biosyntheses. Nor do we understand how all of the diverse parts of this apparatus function synchronously as the cell prepares itself for duplication and cell division.

We do know that, surrounding and penetrating the cell, there is a membrane, and it is the structure and function of this membrane that determines access of the cell to the materials of its environment as well as its susceptibility to external noxious materials. And when one considers the enormous disparity in composition between that which is inside the cell, and that which is without, it is clear that this membrane and its operation are central to the life of the cell. But we know little of its structure and almost nothing of its functioning. Thus, the living object we know best, the single cell, continues to hold many secrets, and their unraveling poses a gigantic task for tomorrow.

But man is not a single cell. And many ask, "As the single totipotent fertilized egg replicates itself, what mechanism ordains some of its progeny to become nerve cells, others brain, kidney, muscle, or blood cells, or prompts still others to lay down calcified bone—when all of these progeny are possessed of the same full complement of genetic information?" No question in biology is so pregnant with implications for the future of man. There has been accumulated an abundance of descriptive observations, but almost no explanatory information is at hand. And there are such derivative questions as: "What is the nature of the clockwork which gives direction and timing to embryonic development? Why does a regenerating liver stop growing when it has attained the size normal to the liver of the species? Why can a lobster regenerate a claw while human amputees are doomed to empty sleeves or trouser legs?" Our gray heads remind us that we know nothing of the time-dependent, presumably irreversible, phenomena which appear to foreordain the length of the human life span.

Our preoccupation with genealogy has been extended far back in time. The demonstration that the familiar amino acids, purines, and pyrimidines, the building blocks for proteins and nucleic acids, are invariably formed when one duplicates in the laboratory the physical conditions alleged to have existed on the surface of this planet several billion years ago, and further, that these are readily condensed to form polypeptides or crude proteins and polynucleotides, suggests that we must recast our view of the origin of life. Rather than the unlikely expression of an event which seemed only remotely possible, was life on this planet virtually inevitable, indeed predictable, given the zero time conditions? This is a surprising turnabout to which I, for one, have not yet adjusted.

The fact of biological evolution is indisputable, but it is time to document it in molecular terms. A beginning in this direction has been made. The peptide chains of hemoglobin, strings of about one hundred amino acids linked head to tail but in absolutely specific order, are expressions of homologous genes throughout the vertebrates; the single peptide chain of a remotely related protein called cytochrome c, similarly, has been found to reflect the presence of a gene which is homologous in yeast and in all animal phyla. The arrangement of amino acids at the active site of at least one enzyme is constant in one bacterium, yeast, rodents, teleosts, and molluscs, suggesting ever more strongly that all living forms derive from common ancestry. The remarkable resemblances, homology if you will, of several pancreatic enzymes suggest that, like the hemoglobin chains, these reflect a process of occasional gene duplication, unrelated to cell division, with subsequent opportunity for remodeling, by mutation, of these now independent genes. But is this the process by which the DNA of cell nuclei increased in amount as animals and plants grew more complex, or did the additional DNA enter from the environment, as viral infection? This distinction is most important if we are to understand our past and, perhaps, our future. Moreover, we should note that we are, as yet, unaware of the biological role of the enormous excess of DNA in the nuclei of our cells. Perhaps 1 per cent of that DNA is required to provide directions for protein synthesis. Does the remainder represent instructions for regulatory processes of which we are unaware or is it totally silent, mutatable, plastic DNA which will find expression in the future when that expression conveys some advantage to the cell?

And while considering evolution, let us note that we still lack understanding of the factors which occasioned or permitted the incredibly rapid evolution of the primates and the almost explosive appearance of *homo sapiens* as we know him today. But are we at the end of the trail? Are we seriously damaging our genetic stock by preserving those who are, in Darwin's terms, unfit? More broadly, can we identify forces which presently condition man's evolution? If so, which way are we headed? Are we still evolving? Or are we, like the sturgeon, coelocanth, or cockroach, to remain essentially constant over eons of time? More to the point still, is it intrinsically feasible to learn how to manipulate our genomes, to correct known hereditary defects, or to hasten our evolution? And if so, should we?

The triumphs of biochemistry in our time have indeed revealed much of the life of a single cell, but we still understand little of the specialized function of organs and tissues or of the modulation of the metabolism of the cells in those organs by messages received from both neighboring and relatively remote cells. Despite years of intensive effort, there is as yet no acceptable description of the mechanism by which any single hormone works. All we have recognized is the gross, over-all consequence of its arrival on a cell surface.

How does a muscle contract? What happens when soft cartilage is replaced by hard bone? In molecular terms how does a kidney—perhaps the organ of evolution par excellence—recognize and accomplish the task of maintaining constant the volume and composition of the blood plasma? We have been conducting clinical electrocardiography for almost fifty years. But what are the chemical events associated with the physical phenomena evident in an electrocardiogram? And some questions are more difficult still. We have a glimmering of understanding of the mechanism by which an impulse is conducted down the axon of a nerve. But what really happens to *initiate* that impulse in the retina, taste buds, or in the skin, much less in the central nervous system? And beckoning to us are problems the social implications of whose solution stagger the imagination. What are memory, learning, anger, love, or imagination? All must have physical representation in the central nervous system. All await exploration.

Fundamental Scientific Research and the Human Condition

Nor is solution of these many problems an empty academic exercise performed exclusively to titillate our imaginations. Armed with the information and understanding thus to be acquired, it is almost certain that one day we shall understand and hence, hopefully, learn to control the major killers of mankind—cardiovascular disease, cancer, and dozens of other disorders. There is now reason to hope that when there has been gathered sufficient understanding of the chemistry and physiology of the brain, the products of our pharmaceutical houses or the skill of our neurosurgeons will successfully displace the practice of psychiatry. Our current ignorance of the essential nature of the human aging process screens us from any reasonable vision of the potential useful and enjoyable life span of future man.

Thus there is every reason to believe that tomorrow's biology will be even more exciting than is that of today and in all likelihood even more immediately applicable to improvement of human welfare. We require better understanding of photosynthesis, plant genetics, and particularly of ecology, together with sufficient understanding of the factors which determine the productivity of the sea, if we are to minimize the number of humans who must go to bed hungry. But these adventures are neither simple nor cheap. They cannot be accomplished by a few isolated adventurers and will require a huge effort involving large numbers of investigators trained and equipped as never before.

And I must warn you that the insights to be afforded by modern biology will also bring terror. Understanding of man at the molecular level will certainly seem to deprive him of his essential mystery, to make even more painful the ancient questions: "Who am I?" and "Why am I here?" And if, as certainly seems one day to be possible, we shall manipulate human genetics or raise, in vitro, human embryos derived from the deliberate mating of genetically culled sperm with genetically understood eggs, it will require a convulsive upheaval on the part of humanists, philosophers, clerics, and jurists to cope with the tortuous problems which shall have been raised. At the ceremonies marking the bicentenary of the Smithsonian a few weeks ago, Robert Oppenheimer noted that those events in science which have had the most marked effect on human thought are those which revealed scientific truths which dramatically overthrew widely held beliefs. Probably the last such event in the history of biology was acceptance of Darwinian evolution. And the next may well be the day when the concepts of paternity and maternity lose their classical meanings, concepts already shaken by the occasional practice of artificial insemination. Please understand that that day is not tomorrow, but it well may be the day after tomorrow.

At this juncture there are those who might find comfort in harking back to the precept in Ecclesiastes, ". . . for it is not necessary for thee to see with thine eyes those things that are hid." But this proscription is not acceptable. We have ignored it for the last century and in so doing have revolutionized our society.

The revelations of physical science have completely altered the world about us and provided us with extensions of our endowed senses. Our economy has been transformed from one based on access to a few raw materials and brute power— that of the industrial revolution—to one based in large measure on the products of man's imagination and his perception of the physical universe –that of the scientific revolution. Moreover, it is the wealth and abundance so garnered which undergird the social revolution of our time. There have always been those who urged social and political change to achieve a reduction in poverty, extension of education to a broader segment of society, and more general access to the best of medical care. These processes have been accelerated in the last year as never before in history. A booming economy, spurred on by the products of modern technology, not only enriches the lives of most of us, at least in a material sense, but has engendered an atmosphere of heightened concern of man for his fellows. This is simply one more rung on the ladder we have been climbing throughout history. Kindness to horses was rare in human society until horses were no longer required for their horsepower. Slavery was abolished at various times and in various countries, not when man grew ashamed, but when slaves could be replaced by other means for the performance of work. Child labor laws and special laws protecting women at work were passed only after our economy could tolerate their passage. Today, when fewer hands are required to produce more wealth, when abundance is evident throughout the land, the civil rights movement and the war against poverty, previously almost unthinkable, are progressing at a significant pace. The Great Society rests not so much on a suddenly heightened compassion as on the surging abundance of the scientific revolution. In the short space of fifteen years we have had dramatically illustrated the principle enunciated by Vannevar Bush in "Science, the Endless Frontier." He said that, "Basic research leads to new knowledge; it provides scientific capital, creates the funds from which this practical application of knowledge must be drawn. Today it is truer than ever that basic research is the pacemaker of technological progress." The last fifteen years amply testify to this prophecy. There is no reason to think that the future will be otherwise.

And so, too, must it be in biology. Like the mountain-climber, we must examine ourselves because we are here. That same sage in Ecclesiastes also stated that, "There are many things greater than these hidden from us for we have seen few of His works." And we have no choice but to go forward and see all we can. With each accomplishment, man may have to reconsider his position, to make appropriate readjustments in the nature of society. But that way lies progress and an ever more rich and exciting life for each of us and our children's children.

If, then, the continually keener insight into man and his universe to be provided by scientific research is the leverage with which society will improve the human condition while providing intellectual excitement, ferment, and a sense of purpose for all, how shall we foster this enterprise? Permit me to express my own philosophy and develop some guidelines for those who must bear this responsibility.

Science, the Federal Government, and the Structure of the University

There has been increasing concern with such problems as geographical distribution of research funds and pressure for the development of a number of "centers of excellence." And there has been increased concern that decision-making occur at the institutional rather than at the federal level. The politically and socially sensible goal for greater geographical distribution of funds in support of research is certainly compatible with the best interests of science—provided that the means which are undertaken are measured and temperate. Otherwise we shall find ourselves in a position analogous to that of the school board which passed three consecutive resolutions—to build a new school, to utilize to the maximum extent possible all materials that could be salvaged from the old school, and not to close the old school until the new school was ready for occupancy. It will avail us naught to destroy that which is successful in our national scientific endeavor by attempting to distribute scientists evenly over the map of the United States in less than critical masses. Successful modern science requires at least minimal aggregations of scientists, aggregations of talents which both reinforce and complement each other. Let us indeed encourage the development of new centers of excellence but at a measured pace timed to the availability of newly trained talented young people.

However the funds be transferred, and whether in support of scientific research, of education in science, or in support of the humanities and arts by the new Foundation, the philosophy which Senator Warren G. Magnuson built into the act which created the National Science Foundation must remain paramount. The transfer of federal funds to the university must not transform the relationship between the university and the rest of American society. The university must not become subservient or the creature of the federal government by virtue of this financial dependency. The essence of the university is its detachment and objectivity, its freedom to serve as constructive critic of our society and our government. These principles have been safeguarded to date in the operation of most federal agencies which support academic research. Even though the totality of such support grows by an order of magnitude, as one day it must, these relationships must remain unaltered if both the federal government and the university are best to serve the American people.

There is, however, a swelling undercurrent which is concerned that university-based research, on its own initiative, is insufficiently sensitive to the pressing problems of our society. This has led to suggestions that there be developed, on university campuses, as an integral aspect thereof, institutes, each of which would be dedicated to multidisciplinary research on a specific overt problem manifest in our society. Certainly I agree that the research activities of the university should contribute to the solution of problems arising out of our social needs. While fundamental research is closest to the hearts of most university scientists, we must be acutely cognizant of the needs of our society. Only a few examples need be cited. It is true that man has been fouling his nest for a long time and that the problem of environmental pollution grows rapidly more acute. The problems generated thereby cannot be solved by the second- or third-rate scientist. And I am particularly concerned that these problems may be attacked by short-sighted individuals who fail to appreciate that pollution is but one aspect of the over-all task of guarding the ecological system in which we all dwell. If some of the best of American scientists cannot be enlisted in this effort, then surely shall we witness the prophecy of Ralph Waldo Emerson, that the human race is doomed to die of too much civilization.

Most of us feel rather strongly about the population problem. But I remind you that the necessary biology is by no means in hand. Our understanding of reproductive physiology is not sufficient to assure the success of our efforts in population control. Nor are the relevant demographic or cultural problems sufficiently understood. Mass transportation, city planning, and adjustment to automation are other problems obviously worthy of consideration within the university. Most academic effort surely will continue to be addressed to the fundamental problems of science, and this is as it should be. Experience has demonstrated that this is the way academic science best contributes to our civilization. But we must also be tolerant of and give approval to heightened interest on the university campus in the applied problems of modern society. That does not mean that we should necessarily recast our academic structures accordingly or substitute, for disciplinary departments, multidisciplinary institutes, each of which is addressed to a different social need, no matter how urgent the problem may be. There are such institutes at universities, but, in the main, these arose spontaneously and by local initiative. A few more, nourished with federal funds, would do little harm. But down what trail shall we have started? Is this to be the price of federal support? Is every federal agency—DOD, NASA, NIH, Commerce, AEC, FAA, Urban Affairs, etc, etc.—to use the carrot-and-stick technique as it plants increasing numbers of foreign bodies on campus? I am not seriously concerned if such institutes are *at* the university, but the future is grim if it is expected that they be *of* the university. At best, such institutes may be a diversion and a nuisance; at worst they could be a menace.

The rationale underlying such proposals derives from the fact that American experience has shown that research flourishes when coupled to the educational process—in contrast, for example, to the soviet system. But this seems disingenuous. There are many important areas of research, which, by their very nature, seem foreign or inappropriate on the academic scene, e.g., weaponry or the survey aspects of toxicology. Moreover, we have examples of superlative research in organizations without formal tie to the educational world—the Beltsville labs of the Department of Agriculture, the Bell Laboratories, the Bureau of Standards, and the National Institutes of Health.

In a general sense, applied research on the campus should probably be limited to the search for generic solutions to important general problems rather than specific solutions for narrow and immediate problems. University scientists can and should contribute to solution of society's problems, and new institutional forms may well be desirable. Current mechanisms for fostering multidisciplinary research on the campus are certainly imperfect. But let us create new forms with the greatest caution.

Guidelines for the Support of University of Science

As we enter the era in which block transfer of funds from the federal treasury to the university becomes an increasingly significant aspect of our research support system, those in responsible positions must never forget that the central figure in the advance of science is the individual scientist. The mechanism which has brought American science to its current position is the research project grants system, wherein each applicant scientist is judged by a jury of his peers. That system should not be altered unless one is absolutely certain that its replacement will function at least as well.

As the agencies which support science have recognized and attempted to meet new needs, each has proliferated an increasing number and variety of programs. And the arts of grantsmanship have grown ever more complex. May I suggest that the time is at hand to reduce this assemblage to the minimum number of programs adequate to the task. In my view this can be done by the following:

1. The individual research project grant, awarded on the scientific merits of the proposal and the competence of the applicant as judged by experts in the field and providing for the specific needs of the applicant scientist and his research.

2. Large grants to the university or college, permitting it to generate new undertakings, such as creation of a new department, construction of new buildings, development of an expensive new facility—for example, a marine biology station, an observatory, or a high energy particle accelerator—or simply to strengthen the totality of research and instruction in

science by addition of new faculty or physical re-modeling.

3. Free funds, to be used by the university or one of its schools as it sees fit, in support of science. Of the various grant programs here considered, only this can sensibly be managed by a calculated formula.

4. National competitive fellowships, with stipends sufficiently high as to carry considerable prestige.

5. Grants to consortia of universities to build and manage unusually large and expensive research facilities.

But one set of needs will then remain unmet, and their sum is serious. While science has burgeoned and the individual scholar has become ever more productive, he has, however, also been increasingly burdened by the very machinery created to foster his scholarly efforts, the project grants system. An increasing fraction of his effort must be devoted to the drafting of applications, preparation of progress reports, self-justification to panels of visitors, bookkeeping, conflict with auditors—those of both the university and supporting agencies—quarrels with the university purchasing agent, all at the emotional and physical expense of research itself. The ivory tower which once offered opportunity for contemplative scholarship has been replaced in some part by a relatively frenetic enterprise. And the chief assets of this enterprise, the scholar's insight and imagination, can be seriously threatened; his effectiveness both as investigator and teacher may be endangered. Now, to some, this might seem but a reasonable description of a real man in a real world. The scientist or scholar, they hold, should no more live *in utero* than the rest of us. But this is a specious argument. The investigator need not be pampered, but no purpose is served by his being hampered. No one of these annoyances is, of itself, serious. But their sum may constitute a significant diversion, a loss of time, and a drain on his personal resources. Even in their absence, the scientist must yet contend with the fierce competition of the equally real world of the scientific community.

Accordingly, I would relieve him, to as great an extent as possible, of the onerous aspects of the research grants system. Unhappily, I have little confidence in the ability of the university, as presently constituted and organized, to arrive at decisions concerning whether a given professor should be supported at the rate of $100,000 or $10,000 a year, much less deny him support. These are cruel decisions, but they must be made. And the current mechanism, which employs faceless panels, juries of peers which meet periodically in Washington employing criteria which are unrelated to age, academic rank, period of servitude, or status in a local power structure, has enjoyed huge success. It is for these reasons that I propose the sixth and final form of research support.

6. Block grants to the largest units on the campus which can sensibly be subjected to external peer-group evaluation, usually an academic department. There is required here an obvious caveat: professors insist that funds be placed in their hands, presidents

urge that more funds be made over to the university, and I, a department chairman, am suggesting that the department or other coherent, formally organized group, is the appropriate unit with which the federal establishment should now become concerned.

But such grants could underwrite the research service supporting organization of the institution, provide for common equipment and service personnel, assure the continuity of ongoing programs, provide the minimal research support required by unestablished junior faculty, and thereby obviate the necessity for much of the entrepreneurial and management activity of the senior investigator while the project grant system provides for his specific needs.

In addition, such block grant support should assure the stipends of most of the graduate students in residence. I have long thought it almost immoral that we have bootlegged much of our support of graduate education by providing, to graduate students, stipends as research assistants defrayed from research grants made to their mentor. This could readily be avoided, and a beginning in this direction is already under way in the "training grants" available from several agencies. Finally, such grants would provide a ready means whereby the federal establishment could strengthen "pockets of excellence" in otherwise relatively undistinguished institutions.

With sufficient experience with a system in which the totality of federal grants programs in support of research and graduate education had been reduced to these complementary packages, we would, one day, know in which direction the system should further evolve.

Responsibility of the University Scientist to Collegiate and Secondary School Education

Finally, to my academic colleagues, let me say that those of us in academia have no role more significant than that of assuring the scientific literacy of the American people. We owe it to our students to abolish the distinction between the arts and the sciences, to convince them that science *is* one of the humanities in our time, and to provide them with instruction in science which is essentially an aesthetic experience rather than a journeyman apprenticeship preparatory to joining us in the profession. It is no cliché to state that the pursuit of science is the pursuit of beauty as well as of truth. The apparent dichotomy created by our curricula, and particularly the nature of our introductory courses in science, has placed science in false perspective and in so doing has unwittingly fostered the traditional American, dominantly utilitarian, approach to science. Science is the most liberating of the liberal arts, and we should abolish both the use and connotations of the term "College of Liberal Arts *and* Science."

In my view the American public will today, happily, adopt an attitude with respect to science similar to that which once prevailed in Europe when science was "natural philosophy" rather than merely the mother of invention. Increasingly, science will be fostered and research supported by our government not only because its derived technology prolongs and makes our lives more comfortable but because science enhances our perception of the world about us. But only if science is understood by nonscientists. How, then, can this be done? The National Science Foundation has taken the lead in arranging for the development of new course content materials, new curricula for instruction in science at every age level, kindergarten through college. Such materials can be prepared only by the sophisticated scientist who is steeped in the lore of his discipline and who has real insight and understanding of its principles, methodology, and implications for society. It is, therefore, imperative that the intellectual leaders of the community of university scientists participate in this important new enterprise if we are to insure that undergraduates, not only from the handful of institutions endowed with such a faculty, but from all our colleges, may leave the campus comprehending that understanding of the physical and biological world renders it more rather than less wondrous, that just as courses in music, art, and literature have prepared them for appreciation of the related forms of beauty, so too can minds prepared in science better appreciate and relish the sight of a green plant, snow, the Milky Way, or a newborn babe.

We will be successful only when Americans in all walks of life understand why the language of the scientist is indistinguishable from that common to all aesthetic experience when describing the technique of an experiment—"elegant," "beautiful"—the manner in which it compels conclusions—"overwhelming," "forceful," "masterful"—or the aspect of nature which has been revealed—"exquisite," "magnificent," "breathtaking." Most importantly, it is the practice of the scientist, rather than the facts of science, which must be given emphasis. Science is ethically neutral. But the course of scientific investigation compels those very traits which the humanists seek to instill—independence, freedom, honesty, imagination, and critical analysis. Hopefully, these habits sometimes carry over into our private and social lives as well. And if education in science, the modern humanity, accomplishes no more than that, our nation, wealthy beyond any previous dreams of man, can well afford to devote a tiny fraction of its gross national product to the ennobling pursuit of beauty, thus perceived.

LYNDON B. JOHNSON
President of the United States

Appendix:
Strengthening Academic Capability
for Science Throughout the Nation

Memorandum from the President
to the Heads of Departments and Agencies

A STRONG and vital educational system is an essential part of the Great Society. In building our national educational system, we must bear in mind all of the parts, and all of the levels—from Head Start for preschool children to the most advanced university levels. At the apex of this educational pyramid, resting on the essential foundation provided for the lower levels, is the vital top segment where education and research become inseparable. The Federal Government has supported academic research in agriculture for over a half century and in the physical sciences, life sciences and engineering since World War II; the returns on this national investment have been immense.

Of the $15 billion which the Federal Government is

spending in research and development activities this year, $1.3, or about 9%, is spent in universities. The $1.3 billion, which includes only Federal research grants and contracts, accounts for about two-thirds of the total research expenditures of our American colleges and universities. Over 25,000 graduate students in engineering, mathematics, physical and life sciences are supported indirectly by employment under these research grants and contracts. Plainly the Federal expenditures have a major effect on the development of our higher educational system.

The strength of the research and development programs of the major agencies, and hence their ability to meet national needs, depends heavily upon the total strength of our university system. Research supported to further agency missions should be administered not only with a view to producing specific results, but also with a view to strengthening academic institutions and increasing the number of institutions capable of performing research of high quality.

The functions of the Federal agencies in relation to the strengthening of academic institutions are as follows:

a. The National Science Foundation continues to have responsibility for augmenting the research capabilities of academic institutions in all fields of science through the support of basic research and research facilities and through measures for improving the quality of education in the sciences;

b. The Department of Health, Education and Welfare will contribute to the over-all development of colleges and universities and to the development of health professional schools, particularly through programs of the Office of Education and the Public Health Service;

c. All Federal agencies with substantial research and development programs have an interest and need to develop academic capabilities for research and scientific education as a part of their research missions.

To the fullest extent compatible with their primary interests in specific fields of science, their basic statutes, and their needs for research results in high quality, all Federal agencies should act so as to:

a. Encourage the maintenance of outstanding quality in science and science education in those universities where it exists;

b. Provide research funds to academic institutions under conditions affording them the opportunity to improve and extend their programs for research and science education and to develop the potentialities for high quality research of groups and individuals, including capable younger faculty members;

c. Contribute to the improvement of potentially strong universities through measures such as:

—Giving consideration, where research capability of comparable quality exists, to awarding grants and contracts to institutions not now heavily engaged in Federal research programs;

—Assisting such institutions or parts of institutions in strengthening themselves while performing research relevant to agency missions, by such means as establishing university-administered programs in specialized areas relevant to the missions of the agencies.

Funds for these purposes should be provided on a scale and under conditions appropriate to the mission of an agency and in accordance with any government-wide policy guidelines which may be established.

Departments and agencies should carefully assess the degree to which and the manner in which their existing programs support this policy, and, when indicated, should use a larger proportion of their research funds in accordance with the intent of the policy. The means for attaining this objective will be determined by each department and agency. In carrying out the policy, the various Federal agencies supporting research at a university should act in concert to a greater degree in making decisions, so as to make the university better able to meet the collective needs of the agencies and to make the Federal support most effective in strengthening the university.

My Special Assistant for Science and Technology, Dr. Donald Hornig, with the help of the Federal Council for Science and Technology, will follow the response of the departments and agencies to this policy. I have asked him to obtain monthly progress reports and submit them to me.

Statement of the President to the Cabinet on Strengthening the Academic Capability for Science Throughout the Nation

Throughout the postwar years, it has been my abiding and actively-supported conviction that the policies of this nation in support of the advance of science would have a decisive role in determining the extent to which we fulfill our potential as a nation—and a free society.

On occasion, during these years, there have appeared attitudes almost medieval in their myopia toward the meaning and promise of the growth of human knowledge. Happily, these attitudes have not prevailed and our national policies have been guided by reason, light and faith in the future of man. As a result, American science today leads the world—free, unfettered and devoted to the ends of bettering the condition of man in every land.

I say this, by way of preface, because I am proud of the part I have been privileged to play—in the Congress and as Vice President—in opening the doors through which we have moved to some of our most significant scientific gains. Now, in this office, I am determined that we shall marshal our resources and our wisdom to the fullest to assure the continuing strength and leadership of American science and to apply the information yielded by its inquiry to the problems which confront our society and our purposes in the world.

Our policies and attitudes in regard to science cannot satisfactorily be related solely to achievement of goals and ends we set for our research. Our vision in this regard is limited at best. We must, I believe, devote ourselves purposefully to developing and diffusing—throughout the nation—a strong and solid scientific capability, especially in our many centers of advanced education. Our future must rest upon diversity of inquiry as well as the universality of capability.

This is very much a concern and a responsibility of the Federal Government and all the Departments and Agencies of the Executive Branch.

Today the Federal Government is spending $15 billion annually on research and development activities. Nine percent of this—$1.3 billion—is being spent in our universities on research grants and contracts. Additional sums are spent for educational purposes such as fellowship or training grants and the programs provided by the Higher Education Facilities Act or the National Defense Education Act.

The impact of these Federal funds is significant. They account for about two-thirds of the total research expenditures of colleges and universities. The manner in which such funds are spent clearly has a most important effect upon advanced education in this country and upon the future of our nation's universities.

Almost all of the Federal research money is provided to produce results that are needed now and in the future to achieve our many national goals in health, in defense, in space, in agriculture and so on. Of the total provided to universities, 34 percent comes from the National Institutes of Health, 23 percent from the Department of Defense, 9 percent from NASA, 6 percent from the AEC, and 4 percent from Agriculture. Only 13 percent is provided by the National Science Foundation—the only agency which supports science and science education as such.

The purpose of the new policy statement I am issuing today is to insure that our programs for Federal support of research in colleges and universities contribute more to the long run strengthening of the universities and colleges so that these institutions can best serve the nation in the years ahead.

At present, one-half of the Federal expenditures for research go to 20 major institutions, most of which were strong before the advent of Federal research funds. During the period of increasing Federal support since World War II, the number of institutions carrying out research and providing advanced education has grown impressively. Strong centers have developed in areas which were previously not well served. It is a particular purpose of this policy to accelerate this beneficial trend since the funds are still concentrated in too few institutions in too few areas of the country. We want to find excellence and build it up wherever it is found so that creative centers of excellence may grow in every part of the nation.

Under this policy more support will be provided under terms which give the university and the investigator wider scope for inquiry, as contrasted with highly specific, narrowly defined projects. These and many more actions will increase the capacity of our universities to produce well-trained scientists and to serve as a source of the ideas on which our national welfare depends.

By adopting this policy, I am asking each agency and department with major research responsibilities to re-examine its practices in the financing of research. I want to be sure that, consistent with agency missions and objectives, all practical measures are taken to strengthen the institutions where research now goes on, and to help additional institutions to become more effective centers for teaching and research.